OXFORD IN ASIA HISTORICAL REPRINTS

General Editors : JOHN BASTIN AND W. G. BEASLEY

JAN COMPAGNIE IN JAPAN
1600–1817

Son 目 Maan 月 Sterre 星

Nagasaki wood-cut of the Dutch East-India ship *Schellach*, c. 1782

JAN COMPAGNIE
IN JAPAN
1600–1817

AN ESSAY ON
THE CULTURAL, ARTISTIC
AND SCIENTIFIC INFLUENCE
EXERCISED BY THE HOLLANDERS IN JAPAN
FROM THE SEVENTEENTH TO THE
NINETEENTH CENTURIES

C. R. BOXER

OXFORD
IN ASIA
Historical
Reprints

TOKYO
OXFORD UNIVERSITY PRESS
LONDON   NEW YORK
1968

Oxford University Press, Ely House, London W. 1.

GLASGOW NEW YORK TORONTO MELBOURNE WELLINGTON
CAPE TOWN SALISBURY IBADAN NAIROBI LUSAKA ADDIS ABABA
BOMBAY CALCUTTA MADRAS KARACHI LAHORE DACCA
KUALA LUMPUR SINGAPORE HONG KONG TOKYO

Enshu Building, Otsuka, Bunkyo-ku, Tokyo

This edition © Oxford University Press 1968

is an authorized reprint (with corrections)
of the second revised edition published by
Martinus Nijhoff, The Hague, in 1950

Printed by Toppan Printing Co., Ltd., Tokyo

LIST OF CONTENTS

LIST OF ILLUSTRATIONS

PREFACE

This book was originally published in 1936, and went out of print shortly afterwards. With the exception of chapter VII, which has been entirely re-written, this edition is mainly a reprint of the first. Corrections of factual and printer's errors have been made; but the intervening fourteen years have not brought to my knowledge anything which involves making major changes. Since the work is avowedly intended for those who possess a knowledge of Japanese history, the original introduction has been omitted, as smacking somewhat of teaching grandmothers to suck eggs. The opportunity has also been taken to bring it up to date, by inserting in the footnotes and bibliography the necessary references to works bearing on this topic which have been published since 1936.

As explained in the original preface, the title is not pedantically accurate. The Netherlands East-India Company was incorporated in 1602, and its ships first reached Japan seven years later. Moreover, the expression Jan Compagnie, like its English counterpart John Company, does not seem to have been used until the second half of the eighteenth century. The Dutch Company was dissolved in 1798; but, in so far as Japan was concerned, it may be regarded as having survived until the end of the Napoleonic period, since the Tokugawa bureaucracy continued to treat the Hollanders at Nagasaki as its representatives. But even if the dates on the title-page do not coincide exactly with the lifetime of Jan Compagnie, they give a good idea of the period when Dutch influence was most strongly felt.

My debt to European scholars in the same field, of whom Dr. Feenstra Kuiper was the most eminent, has been duly acknowledged. For the most part, however, this work is based on the results of the patient researches of Japanese scholars, such as Professors Shimmura, Koda, Kuroda, and Itazawa,

VIII

who may justly be regarded as the worthy descendents of the
Rangakusha of old. The death of General J. C. Pabst, in
January 1942, after a residence of over a quarter of a century
in Japan, was a sore loss to all students in this sphere as well
as to private friendship. Acknowledgement is also due to Sir
George Sansom, and to Mr. Basil Gray, for pointing out some
slips in the original. Dr. Van Gulik, of the Netherlands Legation
in Tokyo, gave helpful encouragement and advice concerning
the reproduction of the coloured plates. Finally, I should like
to thank Mr. Wouter Nijhoff for undertaking another edition
of this book, — at a time far more unpropitious than that
which I foolishly stigmatised as such in 1936.

December, 1949   C. R. BOXER

I. CARTOGRAPHY AND GEOGRAPHY

Appropriately enough, the earliest cartographical relic of the Hollanders in Japan which has survived to the present day, bears every indication of having come out to the Land of the Rising Sun in the first Dutch ship which ever visited that country, the *Liefde*, ex-*Erasmus*.

I refer to the maritime charts in the Imperial Household Museum at Ueno, which formed the subject of a learned article in the Royal Netherlands Geographical Society's Bulletin by Mr. J. W. van Nouhuys [1].

There is no need to repeat here the arguments adduced by that eminent authority in support of his attribution of these charts to the *Liefde*, an attribution with which the present writer fully agrees. The fact that the charts are signed by their compiler, Cornelis Doedtsz, as having been drawn at Edam just four months before the departure of the *Liefde* with the fleet of Mahu from Rotterdam, is in itself pretty nearly conclusive for such an origin. The possibility of their having been brought to Japan later is exceedingly unlikely, as by the time the next Dutch ships came to Japan in 1609, other and more recent maps would in all probability have been available for use on board.

Unfortunately the Japanese Museum authorities can give no exact indication of when or how these charts came into the possession of the Imperial Household, beyond the fact that they were part of the spoil acquired from the Tokugawa, when the Shogunal House of that name was expelled from Yedo (now Tokyo) in the Imperial Restoration of 1868. This in itself however provides a confirmatory clue of some kind, albeit a very slight one. For the fact that the charts were Tokugawa property prior to 1868, makes it quite possible

---

[1] *Zeekaarten van het schip de Liefde ex-Erasmus uit A° 1598*, in *Tijdschrift van het Koninklijk Nederl. Aardrijkskundig Genootschap*, 2e Serie, Deel XLVIII, 1931, Afl. 5.

that they were originally in the possession of the first Shogun Ieyasu. If this was so, then these charts may originally have been joined together, and been that "Chart of the whole world" which Will Adams showed the disbelieving Ieyasu when the latter asked him how he had come to Japan [1].

It must be stressed in passing that the actual maps are rather of Portuguese than of Dutch origin, as is indeed self-evident from the nomenclature (which is almost exclusively Lusitinian, with a few exceptions like the names of some large countries, *i.e. Bresilien*), and from the *Quinas* or Portuguese Arms emblazoned on the same chart inscribed by Cornelis Doedtsz. The scale of leagues, wind-roses, and the double (but differing) scale of latitude marked in the N. Atlantic chart are also typical Portuguese productions. Doedtsz has in fact done little more than copy some Portuguese chart (or charts) which he had before him, as for that matter did all other Netherland and English cartographers of the time, from the great Jan Huyghen van Linschoten downwards. By the time the *Roode Leeuw* and *Griffioen* visited Japan in 1609, other and fresher material would have been available, and the maps used by those ships would doubtless have contained a far larger percentage of Dutch additions and corrections to their Portuguese forerunners, based on the recent voyages of Houtman, van Neck, Maatelief de Jonge and others [2]. The present charts were clearly copied by Doedtsz from Portuguese orginals of the last decade of the golden age of Portuguese cartography, as exemplified in the works of Fernão Vaz Dourado and Bartholomeu Lasso [3].

Whilst on the subject of the *Liefde* and Will Adams, we may make passing mention of a globe made by the latter when in Japan, showing the North-East and North-West passages,

---

[1] "He (Ieyasu) asked me ... As what way we came to the country. Having a chart of the whole world, I shewed him, through the straits of Magellan. At which he wondered, and thought me to lie." Wieder, — *De Reis van Mahu en de Cordes*, III, p. 75. (L.V. Werken, Deel XXIV). On p. 14 of the same work Dr. Wieder observes, "Onmogelijk te zeggen welke Wereldkaart; Plancius, Mercator, Ortelius of een onbekende." Perchance this map of Doedtsz is the *onbekende*, though there must have been other maps and charts on board.

[2] Though John Saris still used Linschoten's *Itinerario* and maps on his voyage to Japan in the *Globe* in 1611–1613.

[3] Cf charts reproduced in A. Cortesão, *Cartografia e Cartografos Portugueses*. Vol II. Plates 38, 39 and 52.

as well as the provinces of that country in considerable detail. This world-globe was somehow acquired by Adams' Jesuit rivals who had a copy thereof made at their headquarters in Macau. This copy came into the lands of that indefatigable chronicler, Diogo do Couto, the great historian of Portuguese India, to whose praiseworthy scientific curiosity we owe a brief description of it, for unfortunately neither the original nor the copy have survived. This is the more regrettable since from Couto's description it is clear that it was based on Dutch, English, Japanese (and presumably Portuguese) sources, which would have rendered it extremely interesting to all students of cartography [1].

In this connection candour compels us to make mention of Mr. van Nouhuys' strictures on Will Adams' cartographical abilities, which indeed do not seem to have equalled the old Elizabethan sea-dog's undoubted qualifications in other respects, whether as pilot, shipwright or, above all, diplomatist.

It is certain that both the Dutch and English imported maps, globes and charts into Japan during the first half of the XVIIth century, but owing to the vicissitudes of fire and earthquakes, few indeed have survived to this day; and the majority of these are difficult to identify from the cursory references made to them in the original *Dagh-Registers* or other contemporary sources. Amongst those which can be identified with certainty (though they are not perhaps cartographical material in the strictest sense of the term), are two magnificent coloured copper-plate engravings, depicting respectively the siege of Hertzogenbosch in 1629, and the defeat of the English off the Isle de Ré in 1627, which are preserved in the collection of Mr. K. Inabata of Kyoto, through whose courtesy I was enabled to inspect them. They were then mounted as *kakemono* or hanging scrolls. The owner stated that he had acquired them from an old Higo family, which is particularly interesting in view of the fact that we have a contemporary reference to the engraving of the

[1] "E em hum globo que este piloto trazia, de que na China se tirou outro que eu tenho em meu poder, se vem claramente estas duas partes por onde tentarão passar a estas. E postas em graduação esta ilha Iapão com todos os seus reinos ate sobre a terra de Chincungu onde affirmão aver aquellas ricas minas da prata." (Diogo do Couto, *Decada XII*, Livro V. Cap. II. p. 218 of the original Paris edition of 1645).

siege of Hertzogenbosch, being in the possession of the Hosokawa family who were the rulers of Higo province in 1635 [1].

The *Goshuinsen* (*Goshuinbune*), or trading vessels whose
owners had obtained permission under the red seal of the
Shogun to trade with foreign countries, which formed the
short-lived Tokugawa mercantile marine during the early
part of the XVIIth century, also had some connection with
the Hollanders, in that Dutchmen frequently served as pilots
in such vessels [2], and no doubt charts of Dutch origin were
often used on board them. In this respect, as in so many
others, the Hollanders were but following in the steps of their
Portuguese predecessors, for originally these vessels were
compelled by Shogunal edicts to carry Lusitanian pilots, and
such few of their charts as survive to this day, are clearly
identifiable as more or less modified copies or adaptations of
Portuguese originals [3].

The critical years of 1635–1641 which saw the enforcement
of the *sakoku-seisaku* or "closed-country" policy of the third
Tokugawa Shogun, Iemitsu, culminating in the expulsion of
the Portuguese (1639) and the removal of the Hollanders
from Hirado to Deshima (1641), also witnessed the importation of many Dutch geographical works which played a
noteworthy part in aiding the Shogun to come to his momen-
tous decision. So much is evident from the following extract
from a contemporary report of the *opperhoofd* François
Caron, — "[Iemitsu] having ordered for three successive
years, maps, globes and an explanation of the way to Europe,
after investigating the size of the world, the multitude of its
countries, and the smallness of Japan (which hitherto was
otherwise believed) he was greatly surprised, and heartily

[1] Letter of Willem Versteegen, Dutch Agent at Nagasaki to the opperhoofd at Hirado, 25. viii. 1635. Versteegen was called upon to give an explanation of this print,
which incidentally is reproduced on Plate 57 of the *Meiji Izen Yogwa Ruishu* (*Catalogue of paintings and drawings in Western style prior to the Meiji period*) printed at
Kyoto in 1925.

[2] Cf Cocks' *Diary* (ed. Tokyo, 1899) and Adams' Letters *passim*. Nor was this usage
confined to Japan. When Willem Jansz visited Nagasaki in the spring of 1630,
amongst the shipping then in the harbour were a Siamese junk piloted by a Dutchman
named Pieter Jansz. Quick, and two Japanese junks chartered by a Tonquinese embassy, likewise piloted by a Netherlander, Vincent Romeyn. Cf. Coenraedt Cramer's
Journal, (*Rijksarchief. Stukken van S. Sweers. Deel V, fol. 206–236*).

[3] As for instance that used by Kadoya Shichirobei in his voyage to Annam *c.* 1630
and still preserved at Ise.

wished that his land had never been visited by any Christians ...." [1].

The Shogun's curiosity about Western geography was also shared by some of the great nobles, and among the items ordered by the chief (anti-Christian) Inquisitor, Inouye, Chikugo-no-kami and by Iemitsu's uncle, the Daimyo of Kii-no-kuni in this same year, we find listed *'t licht der Zeevaert int latyn*, [2] — incidentally proving that Latin was more generally understood than Dutch in official circles.

This influence exerted by the Hollanders on the geographical conceptions of the Japanese, had its counterpart in the influence derived from native Japanese sources which is discernible on the progress of the Western cartography of Japan. It does not seem to be generally realised that although the Japanese freely copied Portuguese and Dutch worldmaps or maps of the Asiatic continent, they almost invariably improved on the originals in delineating the outlines of their own country. For their geographical conceptions of China, India, Europe and America they were indeed wholly dependent on European sources, but as regards the representation of their own land (or those countries immediately adjacent such as Korea) they by no means blindly accepted their Western prototypes. For instance, the portulan chart of Kadyoa Shichirobei just alluded to, though based on a Portuguese model, as is evident from the typically Lusitanian windrose, loxodrome lines, scale of leagues and even the very material which is vellum, yet depicts the outline of Japan far more accurately than does any contemporary Lusitanian map. The earliest Portuguese map showing the sixty-eight provinces of Japan, and Yezo as an island (contrary to the usual European practice), is Father Antonio Cardim's of *c.* 1646, in itself derived from a Jesuit map based to a large extent on Japanese sources.

A curious example of this Japanese influence on Dutch cartographical knowledge is furnished by the following item which I have not seen quoted elsewhere in this connection. When Maerten Gerritsz. Vries set out with the *Castricum* and *Breskens* on his celebrated voyage in search of the fabled

---

[1] *Dagh-Register Batavia* in voce 21. iv. 1641.
[2] *Ibidem.*

gold and silver islands, believed to lie off the East coast of
Japan in February 1643, he was given by the Governor-
General, Antonio van Diemen, and the Raad van Indië a
number of books and maps as listed in a 'Memorandum of
the books and papers which must be appended to the instructions for the expedition to Tartary' [1]. Amongst these
works in addition to the Atlases of Willem and Johan Blaeu,
as also the *Itinerario* of Linschoten, we find the following under item no. 21 — 'Two sketch-maps of the gold island,
as the same is depicted in the Japanese Beobys'. The word
Beoby(s) is, of course, a corruption of the Japanese *Byobu*
(folding screen), and the depiction of these fabled treasure
islands on contemporary Japanese folding screens is of great
interest. Clearly a *Byobu* with a world-map or one of Japan
thereon, of the type of those now in the collection of Mr.
Ikenaga at Kobe, is the kind of screen indicated here [2].
It is probable that the Japanese derived their notions of
these islands from the Portuguese or Spaniards who first
propagated this myth [3].

More as a curiosity than anything else, I reproduce a
translation of the earliest Japanese account of the gold and
silver islands which I have met with, and which contains a
jumbled allusion to the voyages of Quast (1639) and De Vries
(1643) in search thereof. It is extracted from a well-known
compilation on the foreign intercourse of Nagasaki written
by Nishikawa Joken *c.* 1700 and entitled *Nagasaki Yawagusa*
or *Twilight Tales of Nagasaki,*

> *"Concerning gold and silver tales of various countries, and
> of how the Red Hairs reached an isle of gold.*
> Having been born in the port frequented by foreign
> shipping (*ie.* Nagasaki) for many years I have seen and heard
> a good deal about men's customs, birds, beasts, fishes,

[1] Printed on pp. 32–4 of the *Reize van Maerten Gerritsz. Vries in 1643 naar het
noorden en oosten van Japan,* edited by Leupe and Siebold. (Amsterdam, 1858).

[2] Cf the *Byobu* with maps reproduced in H. Ikenaga's *Hosaibankwa Daihokan,* Plates 9, 127, 128 & 130; also the two reproduced on pp. 11 and 12 of the *Kaikoku Bunkwa Daikan* (Osaka, 1929). The corruption of *Beobos* or *Beobys* for Byobu is also found
in contemporary Portuguese records.

[3] Of the numerous articles and essays written on these fabled gold and silver
islands, the best are, O. Nachod, *Ein unentdecktes Goldland,* Tokyo, 1900; E. W.
Dahlgren, *Les Débuts de la cartographie du Japon,* Upsala, 1911, and the recent article

insects and plants. They are so numerous that it is difficult to write them all down, but they are usually different from things in China and Japan, — the only thing that Westerners and Chinese have in common being a lust for gold and silver bullion, in searching for which they freely risk their lives and fear no dangers [1]. Japan is not the only country which abounds in gold and silver, but although there are vast stores of these precious metals in other countries, yet their inhabitants are not so skilled as the Japanese who know how to mine deep in the bowels of the earth.

In some cases the rulers of these lands prohibit excavating and mining operations, for the reason that the lust for gold is apt to sap the morals of the country; in other lands they think that abundance of gold and silver leads the people to adopt luxurious habits which afterwards plunge them into poverty, and it is said that one country has even passed a law prohibiting the increase of the coinage in circulation. Chosen (Korea) has laid the foundation of the state on simplicity, whilst in the writings of Bosai we read that in countries which are rich in gold and silver, the people become greedy and treacherous. However the Barbarians and Red-hairs are not of this opinion, and specially seek to gather gold and silver from everywhere to store up in their own lands.

In the Kwanei period (1624–1643), at the time when the Red-hairs still visited Hirado, one of their ships coming to Japan was blown off her course by a typhoon to the Eastern sea off Nambu, and on sighting an island they sent off a landing party in the ship's boat to fetch water. Because the sand and stones of that island were all of yellow metal, they tried to take it to the ship, but when they put it in the boat it could not move. Try as they would, they could not get the boat to budge an inch, and as the light was fading and night was fast approaching, they thought the God of the island was begrudging them his treasure; they therefore reluctantly

of E. Chassigneux, *Rica de Oro et Rica de Plata* in *T'Oung Pao*, Vol. XXX, 1933. Cf. also G. Kiss, *The Cartography of Japan during the middle Tokugawa Era. A study in cross-cultural influences*, (*Annals of the Association of American Geographers*, Vol. XXXVII, June 1947, No: 2, pp. 101–119).

[1] This recalls Kaempfer's quotation of the Latin saying *Quid non morsalia pectora cogis auri sacra fames* àpropos of the behaviour of the Hollanders at the time of the Shimabara revolt.

decided to throw all the gold dust overboard, and no sooner
had they done so, but they were enabled to row back to their
ship. Well, when they got back to Hirado and discharged the
cargo of this vessel in the haven of Kawauchi, they found
some of this gold dust in the hold, which when put into
water turned it into *saké*. Likewise the local inhabitants
used some in the decoration of their *wakizashi* [1] as I have
heard tell from eyewitnesses. From this time onwards in
world maps, there are a gold and a silver island represented
in the sea to the East of Japan, of which this island may be
the former.

Subsequently the Red-hairs made inumerable efforts to
find this island, and finally a ship supplied with provisions
for two or three years scoured the Eastern seas of Japan in
search thereof, but it had disappeared. Or perchance the
fogs and mists which are thicker and more frequent in this
ocean than elsewhere, wrought some kind of a strange transformation which hid this golden isle from view, without its
having actually disappeared beneath the waves. On the whole
it may be said that this ocean is the roughest sea in the world,
where strange things often happen as the Barbarian (*ie.*
Spanish and Portuguese) ships have found.

Well, this aforesaid Red-hair ship made landfall on the
coast of Nambu in order to take in some fresh water, for
which purpose the ship's boat was sent ashore with five or
six men therein. The local inhabitants being suspicious of
their intentions seized three of them, whereon the remainder
fled to their ship which at once put out to sea. The three
prisoners were sent from Nambu to Yedo. Some of these three
had previously been to Hirado several times, and asked in
Japanese for a certain Hirado man named Shidzuku who was
a close acquaintance of theirs. Thereupon an order was sent
to Hirado for this Shidzuku to come in all haste to Yedo
where he met the Red-hairs who rejoiced exceedingly to see
him. Shidzuku commiserated with them, and thanks to his
clear explanation to the authorities, their doubts were resolved and he was sent with the Red-hairs to Nagasaki. The
time of their arrival in this port, coincided with that of the

[1] *Wakizashi.* — a short sword worn at the waist, together with the *katana* or long
sword, by men of samurai rank.

annual Red-hair ships, on board of which these three people
were sent away. Meanwhile Shidzuku remained at Nagasaki
where he settled as an official interpreter. I know nothing
about the silver island, although in world-maps both a gold
and a silver island are depicted."

This representation of the fabled gold and silver islands
in contemporary European and Asiatic maps, brings us to a
consideration of some very interesting Japanese world-maps
of the Shoho period (1644–1648), which appear to have some
traces of Dutch influence.

Various examples of this type of map are still extant in
Japan, and illustrations of some of them will be found in the
works quoted below [1]. The majority of those which have
survived are painted on folding screens, but one type is
printed from wood-blocks and subsequently hand-coloured.
This particular map, an example of which is in the Ikenaga
collection, is inscribed "published at Nagasaki harbour in the
Hinoto Tori (younger brother of fire and the cock) year of the
Shoho era". As this particular cyclical date does not exist in
the Shoho era, doubt has been thrown on the genuineness of
this print, as also its alleged Nagasaki origin. This question
will be discussed later, when we come to deal with the origin
and dates of Nagasaki wood-block prints. Here it is only
necessary to repeat that whether this particular print dates
from the Shoho era or not, similar types of *mappa-mundi*,
which undoubtedly do date from round about this epoch,
have survived to this day, one of which I once had the
opportunity to examine.

The original is painted on a six-leaf folding screen, belonging, if I remember rightly, to a private collector in Osaka,
but unfortunately I have no record of its dimensions. A very
similar screen in the collection of Baron Masuda of Tokyo, is
illustrated in the catalogue of the *Asahi* exhibition of materials connected with the importation of foreign civilization
into Japan, held at Osaka in 1929 [2]. In the former screen
there are several vessels flying European flags sailing over

---

[1] *Hosaibankwa Daihokan* (2 vols, Kobe, 1932) Plates 127, 128, 130, 133. *Kaikoku
Bunkwa Daikan*, pp. 11–12. G. Kuroda, *Seiyo no Eikyo wo uketaru Nihongwa* (Kyoto,
1924) pl. I.
[2] *Kaikoku Bunkwa Daikan*, p. 11.

different parts of the ocean, in the manner of those depicted
in the Atlases of Blaeu, De Witt, Goos and other contemporary Netherlands cartographers. The particularly prominent is a
finely drawn three-masted Dutch Indiaman shown in full
sail between the Cape of Good Hope and Brazil, whilst other
vessels flying the *princenvlag* can be seen between Java and
Borneo, off Cape Finisterre, and in fight with a Spanish(?)
vessel in mid-Atlantic. Most of the other European vessels
depicted fly the ragged-cross of Burgundy which denoted
Spanish or Portuguese ships; noteworthy are also the Spanish
gallies in the West Indies and off Manilla, and the Chinese
junks depicted in the China sea and off the E. coast of
Madagascar. These details, and perhaps some of the geographical features, are clearly taken or adapted from some
XVIIth century Dutch Atlas (Blaeu?); but the map as a
whole seems to derive from a rather older type, probably
inspired by the TYPUS ORBIS TERRARUM of Ortelius,
such as the Japanese adaptation of this type (likewise on a six-
leaf folding screen) reproduced in Plate 127 of the catalogue
of the Ikenaga collection already referred to. From a cartographical point of view, it is worth pointing out that the
outlines of Japan and Korea are more accurately delineated
than in the probable prototype; that Yezo is shown as an
island; and that the old Ptolemaic conception of a huge land
continent in the Southern Hemisphere is retained, and even
expanded to include New Guinea. This also recalls Portuguese maps of the end of the XVIth century, such as the
Doedtsz copy already alluded to.

In connection whith these Byobu *mappa-mundi*, it may be
mentioned that they are usually of the six- or four- (more
rarely two-) leaf folding screen type; [1] and that they are, or
should be, accompanied by a companion screen (usually two-
or four-leaf) depicting either a large-scale map of Japan with

[1] I have seen a two-leaf one of the Shoho cock year type above alluded to (and
illustrated in Plate 133 of the *Hosaibankwa Daihokan*), with a Dutch ship in the
bottom left-hand corner instead of the Chinese junk depicted in the one actually
reproduced. The *Shinsen Yogaku Nempyo* ascribes the origin of this type to Shoho 4.
(1647). Cf. p. 13 of that work. There is an abridged English translation of this work
by Dr. C. C. Krieger, entitled *The infiltration of European Civilization in Japan during
the 18th century* (Leiden, 1940). The citations in the present work retain their
original page references to the Japanese edition of 1927; and where Dr. Krieger's
version is quoted it is referred to as Krieger, *op.cit.*

its sixty-eight provinces, or else groups of the forty (some-times 42) barbarian races supposed to exist outside of Japan [1]. In one case (the TYPUS ORBIS TERRARUM above alluded to), the *mappa-mundi*, and the map of Japan are each margined by groups of these barbarian countries. This type of map for long continued to be reproduced, but in an increasingly crude and modified form. A very rough specimen is coarsely printed from wood blocks in Nishikawa Joken's *Zoho Kwai-tsusho-ko* published at Kyoto in Hoei 5 (1708). Even towards the middle of the nineteenth century, a version of this map was published as a coloured woodcut by Eijudo of Nagasaki, but the figures of the representatives of the bar-barian countries were brought up to date in one or two instances by the addition of Napoleonic military dress [2].

Apart from probable Dutch influence, whether derived from Blaeu's Atlases or from elsewhere, in these Japanese world-maps of the Shoho period, we have some records, albeit fragmentary, of further influence exercised by the Hol-landers on the geographical and cartographical knowledge of the Japanese during the XVIIth and XVIIIth centuries. A thorough searching of all the Batavian and Deshima *Dagh-Registers* would no doubt yield many references to the impor-tation of maps and globes by the Dutch, but I will confine myself to recording the few instances I have noticed in the course of a cursory glance at the available records in print.

In February 1648 the assistant, Jan van Bijlen, who had accompanied the *opperhoofd* Frederick Coyett on the annual mission to the Shogun's court at Yedo, gave the secretary (*Karo*) of the commissioner Inouye, Chikugo-no-kami, a dissertation on the constitution and position of the United Provinces, illustrating his explanation with a sketch(?) map [3]. In 1657 and again in 1659, the Hollanders presented a world-

---

[1] These barbarian races comprise a medley of European, Asiatic, African and American peoples, the representatives of each race being depicted as husband and wife. They are mostly clad in unrecognizable and fantastic costumes. Only the couples representing Japan, China, and sometimes Holland are clearly identifiable by their costume. The number varies between 40 and 42 as occasionally the Ryukyu, Koreans and Japanese are excluded. Cf. Krieger, *op. cit.* p. 17.

[2] Plate 151 of the *Hosaibankwa Daihokan*.

[3] Journal of Frederick Coyett for 20. ii. 1648 (misprinted 1647 in the citation), quoted by Professor T. Itazawa on p. 28 of the reprint of his article *Rangaku no Igi to Rangaku ni kansuru ni san no mondai* (*Rekishi-Chiri*, vol 59, Tokyo, 1932).

map and two celestial charts as we know from Japanese records [1]. From similar souces we learn that the *opperhoofd* Camphuis presented two world-maps in 1672 [2], probably in response to the demand for a world-map made by the Bakufu in 1668 [3]. Arai Hakuseki in the course of his celebrated interviews with Father Sidotti made use of an edition of Blaeu's Atlas which he possessed (apparently the Amsterdam edition of 1639). In 1710 the Bakufu ordered 1 *Groote Platte Globe* and 1 *Groote Atlas* from the Hollanders, presumably in consequence of their revived interest in the outside world aroused by Arai's interviews with Sidotti [4]. On the occasion of the *opperhoofd* Johan Aouwer's audience with the Shogun Yoshimune in 1717, the celebrated magistrate Ooka, Bizen-no-kami (a sort of Japanese Solomon and the hero of inumerable tales), appeared with an astrolabium of which the Hollanders were asked to explain the use. In the Imperial Household Museum at Ueno in Tokyo, there is still preserved a very fine copper-engraved world-map of the period of Louis XIV and bearing his portrait, which probably came to Japan about this time, and may have been one of the maps alluded to above. It is headed in Latin, *Nova totius terrarum orbis tabula emendata A. N. Visscher* [5].

Nevertheless, despite these importations of cartographical material, it must be confessed that the influence of the Hollanders on the development of cartography in Japan was far less than we might expect. This was probably because most, if not all, of the material imported was either destined as presents for the Shogun, or passed into the possession of Bakufu officials who had neither the wit nor desire to make full use of it. The scholars, astronomers and cartographers who might have made good use of the materials afforded by Western science, were not allowed to learn Dutch, and hence

---

[1] *Ibidem.*

[2] *Tsuko Ichiran, and Tokugawa Jikki* under date of 3. iii. 1671. Cf. also *Shinsen Yogaku Nempyo.* p. 22.

[3] Itazawa's article, *Rangaku no Igi.* p. 33.

[4] *Ibidem,* p. 35.

[5] *Ibidem,* p. 28. Cf. also F. C. Wieder, *Blaeu's Groote Wereldkaart in Japan* (in *Kon. Ned. Aardr. Genootschap,* Vol. LIII, no. 2. pp. 153–5; 1936). The Ueno Museum likewise possesses another version of this map, with a dedication to Bracamonte y Guzman, one of the Spanish delegates to the Congress of Westphalia in 1647–8, substituted for the portrait of Louis XIV.

were compelled to rely rather on the scientific treatises printed by the Jesuits in China. Some instances there are to the
contrary, but they are very few, and the results were meagre.

According to Japanese sources, Western methods of survey
were first introduced during the Kwanei period (1624–1643)
when a man called Higuchi Gonemon of Nagasaki was taught
surveying by a Hollander [1]. Some of this man's pupils founded various schools of land surveying, and one of them
published a treatise on the subject as early as 1687, but it is
evident that their knowledge was superficial and of little
value.

One of the earliest and most celebrated Japanese cartographers, Hojo Ujinaga (1610–1670), is said to have been
taught the principles of geometry and surveying by a gunner
named Juriaen Schaedel, who with three companions was retained by the Bakufu officials at Yedo for about nine months
in 1650, for the purpose of giving lessons in mathematics,
gunnery, surgery and so forth [2]. The value of this instruction
may be questioned, for apart from the fact that Schaedel himself appears to have been merely a humble *Vuerwercker* or
bosschieter, the instruction must needs have been imparted
through the medium of interpreters who knew very little
Dutch and only indifferent Portuguese. Still, Schaedel seems
to have given considerable satisfaction, and perhaps the
relative accuracy of Hojo Ujinga's surveys of Yedo city and
other districts owed something to the Hollander's teaching.
Nevertheless, the scientific knowledge gained by the Japanese
in this connection through Dutchmen or through Dutch

[1] R. Otani, *Tadataka Ino, The Japanese Land Surveyor* (Tokyo, 1932) p. 19. Another
source (*Shinsen Yogaku Nempyo*) states that Higuchi was taught this art in Keian 1
(1648) by a Hollander named Caspar, obviously Caspar Schambergen, who accompanied
the mission of Blockhovius and Frisius. It is worth recording that Nishikawa Joken,
writing *c.* 1690, states that astronomical and cartographical instruments such as
compasses, gnomons, celestial globes and charts, as well as world-maps were made at
Nagasaki in his time, the former being worked in both wood and brass. It is a pity
none have survived to this day, but they were probably nothing more than copies of
Western originals.

[2] Ashida, *Nihon Sozu no Enkaku*, p. 35; Itazawa, *Rangaku no Igi*. pp. 30, 32–3.
Compare also Nachod, *Beziehungen*. p. 328. In the *Dagh-Register*, Juriaen Schaedel is
mentioned as a *Vuerwercker*; he is probably the same man as the *Jurriaen bosschieter*,
oud 27 jaeren, who is listed as amongst those of the crew of the *Breskens* who were
kidnapped at Nambu and brought to Yedo in 1643, as related in the works of Montanus and Nachod.

sources, was insignificant when compared to the debt they
owed to the scientific works published by the Jesuits in China
which became more generally available to all Japanese scholars after the Shogun Yoshimune had lifted the ban on the
importation of these Sino-European scientific works in 1720.
The various calendar reforms and the astronomical observations carried out by the Bakufu officials of the Astronomical
Bureau prior to 1800, were all based in the main on information derived from these Jesuit-Chinese sources [1].

As noted above, the chief reason for this comparative
neglect of Dutch scientific sources, lay in the ignorance of
that language by the Japanese scholars and officials who
could, on the contrary, read the classical Chinese in which
the Jesuits' treatises were composed. In 1745, however, the
interpreters were officially encouraged to learn to read Dutch
books, and not to be content with mere oral proficiency. It
does not appear that the Shogunal Government actually
encouraged the study of Dutch in scholastic circles, but,
contrary to what is almost invariably stated, they placed no
official ban thereon, and in the last quarter of the XVIIIth
century at any rate, freely allowed translations of Dutch
works to be printed and circulated. The result was a notable
increase in the study of Western languages and science during
this period, and in spite of the incapacity or unwillingness of
most of the interpreters to impart their linguistic knowledge
to outsiders, a few Japanese scholars and enthusiasts made
themselves really proficient in the language of the Red-haired
barbarians. This impulse made itself felt in the cartographical
sphere also, of which we may record the following instances.

The celebrated astronomer, Takahashi Yoshitoki, obtained
a Dutch edition of Lalande's work on Astronomy published
at Paris in 1711. With this as a basis, and with information
obtained from other scattered Dutch sources, he so improved
his already profound astronomical knowledge as to be able
to produce work of great accuracy and importance [2]. Not
least of his achievements, albeit an indirect one, was the help
he was able to give the great land-surveyor, Ino Tadataka
(1745–1818), in the course of his monumental twenty-two

[1] *Tadataka Ino*, pp. 18–41.
[2] *Tadataka Ino*, pp. 41–51. Ashida, *Nihon Sozu no Enkaku*, pp. 51–55.

years' survey of Japan, for Ino himself had only the merest smattering of Dutch. Although the astonishing accuracy of Ino's survey, which aroused the justifiable wonder of Von Siebold and Krusenstern, was mainly due to his own painstaking and original methods, yet something at least of his astronomical and mechanical abilities was derived through Takahashi from Dutch sources. In a still lesser degree, Ino's predecessor, Nagakubo Sekisui (1717–1800), who published a map of Japan on a scale of about 1/1,296,000 in Annei 8 (1779) probably owed some of his knowledge to the Hollanders. At any rate he visited Nagasaki in 1765, and is believed to have derived some benefit from the study of Western learning [1].

The Japanese maps obtained by the Jesuits in the late XVIth and in the early XVIIth centuries, and those obtained later by Kaempfer in 1692, were not of course plotted from proper surveys, but were nevertheless more accurate in their general outline than most contemporary European maps of Japan, which were, in fact, successively bettered by the acquisition of this material. Large-scale maps of Japan were compiled during the Keicho, Shoho, Genroku. and subsequent periods, and small-scale maps of the country were printed as early as Kwambun 6 (1666). These large-scale maps of the country (often drawn in several hundred sheets) were merely compiled from panoramic sketch-maps made by each clan or daimiate of its own fief, and reduced to approximately the same scale before being pieced together to form one whole. [2] Even comparatively skilled surveyors like Hojo Ujinaga were ignorant of any theory of map projection, and consequently great accuracy could not be expected. We also look in vain for any sign of Dutch influence, in such ways as the employment of meridians and degrees of latitude and longitude, until the end of the eighteenth century [3].

Apart from cartography in the strictest sense of the word,

[1] Ashida, *Nihon Sozu no Enkaku*, pp. 45–50. *Tadataka Ino*, p. 26–7.

[2] Ashida, *Nhon Sozu no Enkaku*, pp. 32–44. *Tadataka Ino*, pp. 24–5.

[3] Or somewhat earlier, if we are to believe Abel Rémusat, who in his *Nouveaux Mélanges Asiatiques* refers to a Japanese map of 1744 procured by Isaac Titsingh, in which the Japanese had adopted 'la méthode de graduation et de projection, dont les cartes européennes leur fournissaient le modèle." (*N.M.A. Vol. I. p.* 154). Cf. also M. Ramming, *The evolution of cartography in Japan*, article on pp. 17–21 of *Imago Mundi*, Vol II (London, 1937), and M. Kurita, *Nihon-kohan-chizu-shusei* (Tokyo and Osaka, 1932).

the influence of the Hollanders is more perceptible in what may be termed the popular geographical literature of the time. Commencing with the works of Nishikawa Joken, already briefly alluded to, quite a separate class of literature devoted to imparting geographical and sociological information about the outside world (as seen through the window of Nagasaki) grew up during the XVIIIth century in Japan. As the existence of this class of literature, and, more important, the trend of thought which it reveals, has been largely ignored by Western historians (and until lately by Japanese writers likewise) it may not be amiss to devote a little space to it here. The information imparted in these works is often of a very fragmentary or superficial kind, and usually written in a discursive or anecdotal vein, befitting books intended for popular consumption. Nevertheless their contents are not to be despised, and taken as a whole they serve to show that there was far more information about the outside world available to educated Japanese, than most historians will allow. Judging by the variety of copies of such works at the present day, they must have been eagerly read and circulated. The majority were printed at Yedo or at Kyoto, some few at Osaka, and none, curiously enough, at Nagasaki. Extracts from some of the more typical of them will be given later, and here I will confine myself to mentioning a few of those which deal with geographical subjects, and whose contents in whole or in part, are derived from Dutch sources. Lack of space forbids enumeration of more than a few, and therefore only those printed before 1816, will be listed [1].

    1. *Kwai-Tsusho-ko* by Nishikawa Joken. 2 vols. 4 to. Printed at Kyoto in Genroku 8 (1695).

This work is a sort of geographical encyclopedia or compendium, and briefly describes the situation, inhabitants, and products of all countries known to the Japanese at the time. A separate paragraph is devoted to each country, that dealing with Holland amounting to eight pages. The distances from Japan by sea to each country are given in *ri* or Japanese

[1] In compiling this list I have relied mainly on the examples in my own collection, checked, to a certain extent, by the list published on pp. 63–5 of the *Bunkwa inyu ni kan suru kosho tenrankai mokuroku*, edited by Araki and published at Osaka in 1925. Curiously enough, this book is full of misprints as regards the Japanese year-periods, and requires checking with care.

leagues; the appearance, manners and customs of their inhabitants together with their chief products are briefly described. This is the first work ever printed in Japan dealing with foreign countries (other than China or Korea), and is of great interest as giving us an insight into the degree of knowledge of the outside world possessed by educated Japanese at the time of Engelbert Kaempfer's visit to Japan. Some twenty-five years later, the work was reprinted in an expanded form under the title of

2. *Zoho Kwai-Tsusho-ko.* 5 vols.4to. Printed at Kyoto in Hoei 5 (1708).

This edition contains some thirteen illustrations including (i) a grossly printed map of the fifteen provinces of China; (ii) woodcut of (a) Chinaman of the Ming dynasty with his wife, (b) ditto of the Manchu dynasty; (iii) four full page engravings of Nanking and Fukien junks, in the first two volumes which deal with China. Volumes three and four contain (i) double-page world-map of the Shoho type referred to above, and depicting New Guinea (*Nova Kineya*) and Australia (*Shin Oranda* = New Holland) as part of a large land mass in the Southern hemisphere; (ii) woodcut of an Annamite couple; (iii) couple from *Tenjiku* or India; (iv) a Hollander and his wife, the former with the inseparable tobacco pipe. This last woodcut served as a prototype for many subsequent reproductions in books and prints; (v) double-page block of a Siamese junk with its measurements; (vi) large double-page cut of a Red-hair (Dutch) ship, the measurements for this last vessel being on the *verso*. The last volume is a sort of gazeteer and contains no illustrations. This edition is interesting as containing the earliest detailed representations of Dutch men and ships ever printed in a Japanese book. Whilst on the subject of Nishikawa Joken, we may mention another of his works, which although it deals with matters ethnographical rather than geographical, may find a place here.

3. *Yonjuni-koku (or Shijuni-koku) Jinbutsu Zusetsu.* 2 vols. sm. folio. Printed at Yedo in Kyoho 5 (1720).

Depicts a man and woman from each of the 42 barbarian countries, including China(!), outside of Japan. The designs of both figures and costumes are quite the same as in the pictures accompanying the maps of the Shoho era described above; except for the Hollander, who is represented in a costume of *circa* 1680, and evidently drawn from life. Most of the other representations (save that of the Portuguese from Macau) are purely fanciful and derived perhaps from Chinese sources. Contrary to what is usually the case with these works the woodcuts are all carefully executed and finely drawn, being of considerable artistic merit. This first edition has a fine title-page with the characters printed after the Chinese style, which, together with the quality of the paper used, serves to distinguish it from,–

> 4. *Bankoku Jinbutsu Zu.* 2 vols. sm. folio, same place and date of publication.

This is a textual reprint of No. 3 except for the lack of a titlepage and the re-worded heading to the first page which serves as a title to the work. As noted before, the figures in this work are taken from those published in the pseudo(?)Nagasaki woodcut Shoho map, which itself was reprinted in 1708 under the title of

> 5. *Bankoku Zokai Zu.* Published at Yedo in Hoei 5 (1708).

I have not seen a copy of this print myself, but it is briefly described on p. 71 of Araki's *Kosho Tenrankai Mokuroku*, where the minor points of difference between it and its predecessor are alluded to. The next three items are also taken from this same catalogue, but as no details whatever are given therein, I am unable to furnish a description of them. Presumably they are more or less modified reproductions of the Shoho type of world-map.

> 6. *Mankoku shoka no Zu.* Printed in Hoei 7 or 1710, but no place is mentioned. Yedo(?). [1]
>
> 7. *Chikyu Ichiran Zu.* Printed at Osaka in Tenmei 3 (1783).
>
> 8. *Shokoku Shuran no Zu.* Printed at Yedo before 1789 and probably *c.* 1785.
>
> 9. *Sankoku Tsuran Zusetsu.* 1 vol. text in-4to and 5 unfolding maps. Published at Yedo in Tenmei 5 (1785) by Hayashi Shihei of Sendai.

[1] Another version of this map with the cyclical year corresponding to 1710 is also listed in Araki's Catalogue, no place of publication being mentioned.

This celebrated work of the famous scholar and carto-grapher Hayashi (Rin) Shihei of Sendai is well known to all students of the history of Tokugawa Japan; the work having been translated into French by J. Klaproth, and published at Paris for the Oriental Translation Fund in 1832 under the title of *San Kokf Tsou Ran To Sets*. The maps were likewise reproduced in an accompanying Atlas, on the same scale as the original, and with the legends translated into French [1]. The blocks for the original edition together with all copies which could be found, were destroyed by order of the regent Matsudaira Sadanobu in 1792, and its author thrown into prison where he died soon after. Hence complete copies of this first edition of Tenmei are exceedingly rare, though the book subsequently had a wide circulation in manuscript and manuscript copies are often met with. The "three countries" referred to in the title are Chosen (Korea), Ryukyu and Yezo. A map and description of the Bonin group (Mujin-shima or uninhabited isles), is also given. The volume of text contains interesting woodcuts of the Ainu aborigines of Yezo, illustra-ting their manners, customs, dress and so forth which are not reproduced by Klaproth. The five maps are composed as follows (i) general map of Japan, Chosen, Gulf of Pechili, Yezo, Karafuto, Ryukyu and Bonin islands; (ii) Yezo; (iii) Chosen; (iv) Ryukyu and (v) Mujin-shima or the uninhabited isles. From a cartographical point of view the maps are interesting as three of them (general map and those of Chosen and the Mujin-shima) have the degrees of latitude indicated thereon, and in the case of the general map the degrees of longitude between 157° and 171°. In the text of the work, Hayashi Shihei makes mention of a book on Geography shown him by the Opperhoofd of Deshima, Arend Willem Feith (whom he calls *Arento Uirureito Fuheito*), on his visit to Nagasaki in 1777–8. He adds that in this Geography (*Zeogarahi*) the Bonin islands are termed *Woeste Eilanden*. This goes to show that some at least of the information on which he based his maps was derived from the Hollanders.

---

[1] The map and description of the Bonin islands (*Mujin or Munin-shima*) had been previously utilised by A. Rémusat for an article on the subject in Vol. I. of his *Nouveaux Mélanges Asiatiques*, Paris 1829 (Vol. I, pp. 155–170). Rémusat had secured Isaac Titsingh's own copy of the *Sankoku Tsuran*, which the latter had obtained from Japan.

10. *Seiyo Sembu.* 1 vol. 4to. Kyoto, Osaka and Yedo in Tenmei 7 (1787).

Although this work really deals with a collection of European coins formed by Isaac Titsingh's friend Kuchiki Samon, the daimyo of Fukuchiyama in Tamba province, yet it deserves inclusion here as it contains a map of Europe with the national boundaries clearly marked, and as such is the first separate map of Europe to be printed in Japan so far as I am aware. Incidentally there are three editions of the same work, all of slightly different sizes, and with minor differences throughout, published in the same year, the map being omitted in one of them. I can give no explanation for this or distinguish the relative order of publication, but it is possible that the work was issued simultaneously in Kyoto, Yedo, and Osaka, as all three places appear on the last page as being the place of publication. The work was published under the name of Ozawa Toichi, a retainer of Kuchiki, but there is little doubt that the daimyo himself was responsible for drafting most of it, probably with the active assistance of Isaac Titsingh with whom he was on exceptionally intimate terms, and whom he furnished with many Chinese and Japanese coins. Whilst on the subject of this learned daimyo who was one of the leading *Rangakusha* or Dutch scholars of his time, we may mention a work of his quoted in Araki's catalogue although it seems to have remained manuscript. At any rate no publisher or place of printing is mentioned, and I have never seen a copy of it.

11. *Taisei Yochi Zusetsu.* 6 vols. The work is a kind of geographical compendium dealing with Western countries and has a preface by Hatotani Kohei dated *Tenmei* 9 (1789).

Of rather less renown as a *Rangakusha*, but of greater fame as a man of science, artist, dilettante and freethinker was his contemporary, the celebrated Shiba Kokan (1738–1818), author of numerous, one might almost say inumerable works on various aspects of European science, of which he was the apostle *par excellence* amongst his own countrymen. Some account will be given of this remarkable personality elsewhere and here we will confine ourselves to recording his chief geographical works published during this period.

12. *Yochi Ryaku Setsu.* 1 vol. 8vo. Printed at Yedo in the autumn of Kwansei 4 (1792).

This is an excessively rare little work whose existence is unknown even to the principal biographer of Shiba Kokan. Besides my own copy, I know of only one other in existence, — that in the rich collection of Mr. Ikenaga of Kobe. On the verso of the title page is a curious engraving depicting children in classical dress (or rather undress) with a sextant, compasses, globe etc., against a Western-style background. It is obviously taken from some European Geography. This little pamphlet of only 21 pages is further illustrated with two diagrams of the Western and Eastern Hemisphere respectively. Earlier in the same year Kokan had published (amongst a number of other geographical, astronomical and zoological copper-plate engravings), a large world map entitled

13. *Chikyu Zu.* Large unfolding double-page map of the Eastern & Western Hemispheres; copper-engraving published at Yedo in the 2nd month of Kwansei 4 (1792).

This map affords scope for a vast number of interesting considerations, alike in the legends on the map itself as in the various diagrams surrounding it. We have only space here to point out the four interesting inset views (accompanied by brief explanations) of (i) Adam's Peak in Ceylon (ii) The Cape of Good Hope with European shipping in Cape Town roads, (iii) whale fishing off Greenland and (iv) the picture of a narhwal. On the map itself the route of Magellan and other circumnavigators is shown by a dotted line, as is the track of the Dutch Indiamen to Japan and Java, etc. The form of Australia (called both *Nova Oranda* and *Shin Oranda* on this map) joined up with New Guinea (*Nova Guinea*) recalls some of the mid-XVIIth century maps of Blaeu, and the original prototype of this remarkable Japanese copper-engraving was no doubt some Dutch map of about that time. A closer study of this map would certainly carry the identification further. Amongst the other eleven copper engravings published by Kokan in this same year, one of the Pacific Ocean area on a zenithal equal-area projection calls for special mention. Five years later, Shiba Kokan published a compendium explaining the principles of map construction and the elements of geography under the title of

14. *Chikyu Zenzu Ryaku Setsu.* 1 vol. 4to. Printed at
  Yedo in Kwansei 9 (1797).

Curiously enough, although the Preface is dated Kwansei
9, the date of publication is given on the penultimate page as
Kwansei 5, *ie* some four years earlier which is obviously impossible. The work contains several geographical diagrams
(including the two previously printed in the *Yochi Ryaku
Setsu* referred to above) as well as two cuts of a man and
woman from the Coromandel coast and Greenland respectively, — this last presumably to illustrate the effect of extreme
heat and cold on human clothing. For the other geographical
works of Shiba Kokan, the reader is referred to the excellent
study of Professor Muraoka, and we will next list a work by
the great cartographer Sekisui Nagakubo of Mito, Kokan's
elder contemporary.

15. *Oranda Shinyaku Chikyu Zenzu.* Large unfolding
  wood-cut map of the E. and W. Hemispheres.
  Printed at Yedo in Kwansei 8 (1796).

This map is drawn on the same principle as that of Shiba
Kokan's copper-engraving of four years earlier. It is however
much more crudely executed, and lacks most of the interesting legends in the latter map. By way of compensation the
explanatory text printed alongside is much fuller. The map
bears traces of the Sino-European influence derived from the
Jesuit cartographers, though it appears to be chiefly based on
a Dutch model of *c.* 1660 like that of Shiba Kokan. An interesting, and apparently unique feature of this map is that the
Dutch words *Algemeene Waereld Kaart* are twice printed in
Roman type on the stiff outer cover of *karakami* (*lit.* Chinese
paper). Although this map was far below the standard of that
of Shiba Kokan it proved popular enough, and was twice reprinted under the same title in the same year (1796) and at an
unspecified date later. Neither of these two later editions
however have the inscription *Algemeene Waereld Kaart* on
the cover.

16. *Reijusan Zusetsu* by Shiba Kokan. 1 vol. in 4-to.
  Published at (Yedo) in Bunkwa 5 (1808).

An excessively rare little work, not mentioned in any Japanese catalogue or bibliography that I know of. A very slim
volume of only twenty-four pages, it consists of extracts

PLATE I   P. 22

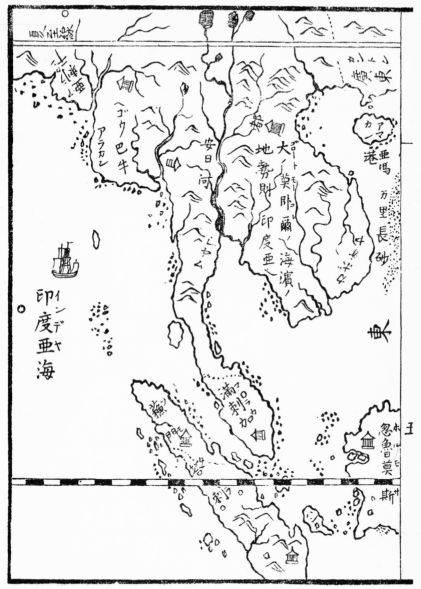

Shiba Kokan's map of Malaya, 1805
Reproduced from his fragmentary translation *(Reijusan zusetsu)* of part of Valentyn's
Oud en Nieuw Oost-Indiën quoted on p. 22 of the present work

relating chiefly to Southern India (Malabar, Coromandel and Ceylon) as translated by Kokan from Valentyn's *Oud en Nieuw Oost-Indiën*, whence some of the woodcuts are also derived.

It was stated at the beginning of this section that only the principal geographical and cartographical materials showing evidence of Dutch influence before 1800 could be recorded in the space at our disposal. Even so, this list of sixteen works is by no means complete, but withal it is sufficient to give a pretty good idea of the standard attained in this respect. From 1800 onwards, works dealing with or influenced by Dutch geographical sources, poured from the presses in an ever-increasing stream which reached its climax during the Tempo period (1830–1843) and the years immediately prior to the Meiji Restoration. However, the majority of these later works are derived not so much direct from Dutch sources as from English, American, French and German, and so lie outside the scope of this essay. The interested reader will find a fairly exhaustive list of such works on pp. 73–91 of Araki's Catalogue, and notices of the majority of them in the *Shinsen Yogaku Nempyo*, and in Krieger's English translation thereof.

II. MILITARY ARTS

It is now generally agreed by foreign scholars who have studied the subject at all carefully, that the Japan of the late XVIth and early XVIIth centuries was more deeply affected by European culture and influence, than was formerly believed. It might also be expected that so warlike a race as the Japanese would have studied the "noble Art Military" as it was practised in contemporary Europe, no less thoroughly than they adopted Western military methods wholesale in the eighteen-seventies. Such, however, was not the case, and whilst such objects as tobacco and potatoes were speedily naturalised, the cannon and musket scarcely progressed beyond the experimental stage. Nor are the reasons for this state of affairs far to seek. For practical purposes Japan's intercourse with European powers from 1542–1854 was limited to two nations, the Portuguese and the Dutch, (for the Spaniards, English and Russians only made feeble and sporadic appearances) and neither of these two races was particularly able, or willing, to teach her the arts of Mars. This was not, of course, through any lack of doughty soldiers in either of these two countries — indeed the Portugal of Albuquerque and the Holland of Prince Maurice could well claim to have been in the vanguard of military progress in their time — but simply because the vast majority of Europeans visiting Japan were merchants first and last, though not all the time.

The Portuguese, it is true, set a high value on military virtues', and, as their historian, Faria y Sousa, wrote, they prized only those of their possessions which were gained with the sword; but on the other hand their victories were due chiefly to their superior spirit and equipment, whilst their discipline and organization were simply non-existent. Every unmarried Portuguese in Asia ranked as a *soldado*. and in time of war, they were grouped haphazard under whichever captain they listed, and disbanded when the campaign was over. Their pay was seldom if ever received, and they lived on plunder in war and on charity in peace [1]. The Dutch, on the other hand, maintained a regular fleet and army in the Indies; their troops were regularly — if poorly — paid, and organized more or less after the European fashion, being subjected to a discipline which was extraordinarily severe; but they only served, naturally enough, in places where the East India Company waged war or maintained garrisons, and these places did not include Japan [2]. From time to time we find bodies of Japanese serving as mercenary soldiers in Portuguese or Dutch service, but this practice was forbidden by the Shogun Hidetada in 1621. The merchants and sailors who formed the vast majority of Hollanders visiting Japan, were not likely to spend much time teaching the arts of war to a race which they regarded as quite formidable enough as it was. Furthermore, the Japanese of those days, who justly prided themselves on their military spirit, were not very likely to have sat at the feet of Southern Barbarian or Red-haired teachers, when they could look back upon some centuries of continuous civil war, and upon Hideyoshi's invasion of Korea, from which to draw endless lessons and speculations.

All things considered then, it is not very surprising that European military influence in Japan from 1542–1853, was confined to the introduction and partial adoption of a few technical inventions such as muskets and cannon, and to the short-lived attempt of Tokugawa Ieyasu to lay the foundations of a Japanese Navy.

Curiously enough, the first Hollander who ever visited Japan — as far as we know — was a gunner. This man, Dirck Gerritszoon of Enkhuyzen, who served as a gunner in various Portuguese ships, came to Japan in the summer of 1585 on board of the carrack *Santa Cruz* and spent seven months in the land of the Rising Sun. He returned to Europe in 1589 in the same ship as his more celebrated contemporary Jan Huy-

[1] For a detailed account of the life of a Portuguese soldier in Asia *circa* 1600, see Diogo do Couto, *Dialogo do Soldado Pratico*. Shorter and more convenient is Botelho de Sousa, *Subsidios para a Historia Militar Maritima da India 1585–1605*, pp. 15–20.

[2] Conditions in the Dutch service are well described in Saar, *Ost-Indianisch 15-jährige Kriegsdienst* (new edition, Nijhoff, The Hague, 1930).

ghen van Linschoten, and reached his native town in 1591. On account of his many years' experience of and travel in the Far East, he received the nickname of "China" and, in later years, he accompanied the pioneer expedition of the Hollanders to the Far East via South America [1]. In all probability several Hollanders and Germans visited Japan in Portuguese service, for most of the gunners on the Lusitanian ships were of these nationalities, but no others have left traces behind them [2]. On board the *Liefde*, which arrived off Bungo in May 1600 with the celebrated Will Adams on board, there was a large supply of cannon and firearms in addition to the ordinary ship's armament. The fate of this ship and her crew has been told too often to need repetition here, and we need only note that the Shogun Ieyasu carefully took out all the guns and ammunition, which were used by Dutch gunners at the battle of Sekigahara in October, according to Diogo do Couto.

With the regular opening of the Dutch Factory at Hirado in 1609, and the appearance of the English there four years later, the importation of guns and firearms assumed an increasing importance. The Shogun and his ministers preferred to receive guns and their appurtenances rather than anything else as presents, and both Dutch and English drove a thriving trade in artillery and ammunition. In 1614 business was particularly brisk, for Ieyasu was preparing to attack Hideyori in Osaka and was buying up all the cannon he could lay hands on. In addition, the Hollanders and English cast ordnance at Hirado, but the Japanese always preferred those cast in Europe, and said that they "would rather have one of those cast in Europe than ten of such as were ever cast in Japan" [3].

These cannon played a big part in the two sieges of Osaka, and even after the fall of that fortress and destruction of the house of Toyotomi in June 1615, the demand for ordnance was not abated.

In the year 1615 the Hollander, Jacques Specx (who had

---

[1] Cf. J. W. IJzerman: — *Dirck Gerritsz, Pomp, alias Dirck Gerritsz, China.* M. Nijhoff, The Hague 1915.

[2] The Lusitaian opinion of the Hollanders was amusingly stated by the Portuguese historian, Barbuda, who wrote that they were "merely good gunners, and beyond that fit for nothing, save to be burned as desperate heretics."

[3] Cf. Cocks' *Diary, passim,* and M. Paske-Smith: —*Western Barbarians in Japan and Formosa 1602–1868,* pp. 26–27.

first arrived in Japan in the *Roode Leeuw met pijlen* in July 1609), presented to the Shogun at Kyoto two iron sakers from the ship *Enchuijsen*, together with 100 round-shot and 350 catties of gunpowder. This present was very favourably received by the Shogun, and when the guns were handed over, Specx informed him that the new Governor-General, Geraert Reijnst, had sent ashore at Bantam two cannon from his own flagship, which would be forwarded later to Ieyasu and Hidetada as presents [1]. From this same ship, *Enchuijsen*, probably hails the cannon with the mark $\mathcal{Y}_E$ which is now in the Military Museum at Kudan, Tokyo.

In the same year, Specx had cast at Hirado a metal gun of 600 lbs. weight, which was destined as a present for "Koshiki president and chief counsellor of the old Emperor", in other words Honda Masazumi, Kozuke-no-suke, who was Ieyasu's chief minister and who appears in Cocks' Diary under the fearful and wonderful guise of "Codskin". Two more cannon were cast at Hirado in the same year by the Hollanders, in order to replace the two sakers from the *Enchuijsen* [2]. The casting of these guns was witnessed by Cocks, whom Specx asked to come and watch the proceedings, on which occasion we may be sure that liquid refreshment was not lacking [3]. The yacht *Jacatra*, which came to Japan in August 1615, took away one of the guns cast by the Hollanders at Hirado, whilst the *Swarte Leeuw*, which arrived in July 1616, took away two or three more. The English *Hoseander*, which arrived in 1615, brought *inter alia* 5 chests of guns for sale to the Japanese.

Naturally enough, the Japanese were anxious to learn the art of casting cannon for themselves, and in 1618 they asked

[1] MacLeod: — *De Oost-Indische Compagnie als Zeemogendheid in Azië, 1602–51*, Vol. 1, p. 306–7.

[2] *Idem.* Cf. Cocks' *Diary* Dec. 26, 1615: "The Hollander had a demi-cannon of brass cast this day, po. 5,000 wight, a very fayre piece."

[3] Cocks' *Diary*, p. 34. (Hak. Soc. Edition). Cocks remarks: 'I . . . . marvelled at their workmanship. For they caried the mettell in ladells above 20 yards from the place where the mould stood, and soe put it in, ladelfull after ladell, and yet made as formal ordinance as we doe in Christendom, both of brass and iron. Capt. Speck tould me nether workmanship nor stuffe did not stand hym in halfe the price it cost them in Christendom." Later (p. 99) he says "the two founders are called Jembio Dono & Scongero Dono." These names are not identified in Professor N. Murakami's edition of the *Diary* (Tokyo, 1899), nor have I been able to trace them.

Jacques Specx for a gunner to initiate them in the mysteries of the fiery art. Specx was anxious to comply with this request, for he realised that if he did not, then they would perforce turn to his rivals, the English, for assistance. Unfortunately, however, there was no one else at his disposal save the gunner of the *Enchuijsen*, Frans Andriesz, who was a bad character and an incurable drunkard. Still, he had perforce to use him as there was "no better stuff", and gave him a severe lecture in the hope of inducing the sinner to mend his ways. But all was in vain; poor drunken Frans could never stay sober for more than five minutes together, so that finally Specx dared not let him go, but promised the Japanese to send another gunner the next year. The daimyo of Hirado also asked for a Dutch cannon, and Specx promised to send him one as speedily as possible [1]. During all this period, the Hollanders used to bring broken and damaged guns to Hirado for repair, in addition to casting cannon there for themselves and the Japanese. At this time the Dutch had no cannon-foundry in the East, and thus Japan was especially useful to them, but some time after the foundation of Batavia in 1619, a cannon-foundry was erected there, and presumably the casting of guns in Hirado was given up after that. This is the more likely, as the Hollanders were, naturally enough, by no means anxious to lay bare the art of casting guns after the European fashion to the eyes of the skilful Asiatics. Thus with regard to the cannon-foundry at Batavia it was reported that it was situated "too close to the view of all and sundry, and in particular the natives and Javanese, from whom this art should certainly be kept secret", and accordingly it was shifted to a less conspicuous place within the Castle walls [2]. In later years, copper from Japan was largely used in the casting of guns in this foundry, but it never attained the fame of the Bocarro's foundry at Macau, and was abandoned about 1690.

Presents of cannon for long continued to be acceptable in Japan, and when in 1627 the Shogun refused to accept the presents offered by Pieter Nuyts (on account of conflicting Dutch and Japanese claims in Taiwan), the daimyo of Hirado

[1] MacLeod, *op. cit.* p. 307–8.
[2] *Geschiedenis der Nederl. Artillerie*, by F. H. W. Kuypers, iii deel., p. 209. General J. C. Pabst drew my attention to this interesting extract.

retained for himself four bronze guns which were included in the rejected treasures [1].

What value the Japanese attached to gunnery and the allied arts, is clear from certain events which are recorded in the local history and traditions of Hirado as having taken place during the captivity there of Pieter Nuyts, former Governor of Taiwan, in the early sixteen-thirties. The Japanese officials and in particular one Furukawa Jibuzayemon, often asked him to teach them gunnery, but he always replied: "Japan rules the land with bow, arrow and sword, my country only with firearms, wherefore I cannot teach you this art." Eventually, however, Nuyts yielded to Furukawa's importunity, it is said, and taught him the whole art of gunnery, in a single room, whilst Jibuzayemon kept his knowledge a secret within his own family [2] It may be doubted whether Nuyts — who was a merchant pure and simple — really knew much about gunnery, or whether he could explain what little he knew in one small room, without any practical demonstration. At any rate, when the Shimabara rebellion broke out in the year 1637–8, and the insurgent Christians shut themselves up in the old Castle of Hara, the Japanese were compelled to call in the assistance of the Hollanders with their ordnance, which shows that they cannot have had much faith in their own prowess with the gun. Other writers have dealt at length with this affair, and we will only mention here some notices of the part played by the Dutch cannon in the siege, which are to be found in Hirado records. Some small 5-pounders were landed from the Dutch ship *De Rijp*, and later on a 12-pounder and other cannon were brought round from Hirado. Not much damage was done from the Hollanders' land battery, but on several occasions the Shogunal commander, Matsudaira Izu-no-kami, the Bugyo of Nagasaki, and others came to watch the Dutch cannon in action. On one occasion — "a piece of the cannon's mouth burst during the firing, whereby the assistant gunner Gylak was struck in the belly, and thrown over the eastern bamboo palisade on to the ground outside

---

[1] MacLeod, *op, cit.* p. 807. In 1636, "2 fraije metalen stukken geschut schietende 6 lbs. ijzer" were sent as presents to Japan. (Letter of G.G. Van Diemen, 2. vii. 1636.)

[2] *Shinkoki, Kashinden, Kameoka Zuihitsu* and other records kindly translated by Mr. J. B. Snellen of the Netherlands Legation, Tokyo, in 1930.

the battery, so that he died" [1]. The small effect of the Dutch cannon was no doubt chiefly due to the situation of the fortress, which could only have been effectively battered with mortars, owing to the high trajectory necessary to throw roundshot or bombs inside the fortifications. Probably this was pointed out by the Hollanders by way of excuse; at any rate we find that they were ordered to cast mortars and to teach the Japanese this art in the following year of 1639.

The preparations were presumably begin in 1638, soon after the Shimabara campaign, for already on February 26th, 1639, we find the following entry in the diary of François Caron, who had just become Director of the Dutch factory at Hirado [2], "one mortar was cast in the presence of the lord of Hirado who had come thither for the express purpose of seeing it." Two days later another mortar was cast, and on March 2nd we read "we were continuously busy with the blacksmiths and silversmiths cleaning and scraping the mortars, which had been turned out very black and corroded." For a whole week they were busy with this task, and with making quadrants of copper and other necessary equipment, but by the 16th of March all was ready, and accordingly the first test was held. All the local big-wigs came to see the fun, and two shots were fired from each mortar. Unfortunately, the four big copper quadrants, each weighing over 140 lbs., and all the carriages and tackle were smashed to pieces by the violence of the recoil, though luckily the mortars themselves were undamaged. The next week was occupied in making new quadrants (this time of iron) and carriages of stronger and better wood. These were all completed by the 23rd March and on the following day Caron left Hirado for the Court at Yedo, taking with him two large bronze mortars, with their equipment of four iron quadrants, two carriages and forty bombs both empty and filled, in addition to one small mortar with two iron quadrants, one carriage and twenty grenades, the weight of the whole being estimated at 6,000 catties, and destined as a present from the East India Company to the

---

[1] Extracts from the *Temmaibun*, translated by Mr. Snellen.
[2] What follows is taken from the original unpublished MSS. *Dagh-Register* of Hirado 1639, in the Hague Archives. Compare also pp. xlvii-*l*, of my edition of *A True Description of the Mighty Kingdoms of Japan and Siam*, (London, 1935).

Shogun Iemitsu. From Hirado to Osaka, which was reached on April 3rd the journey was made by sea, but from Osaka to Yedo, the whole train had to be carried overland along the old Tokaido way, by 300 coolies at the Shogun's expense. The difficulty of handling this clumsy material over the Hakone mountains must have been considerable. Caron reached Yedo about the end of April and the mortars arrived a few days later being placed in the garden of the daimyo of Hirado's *yashiki*. The next few weeks were taken up with discussing the mortars, and the method of testing them; finally on the 16th of June they were moved by 260 men from the daimyo's garden to the firing ground selected on the outskirts of Yedo, at Azabu, where a piece of land measuring 70 feet by 90, with five houses erected on it, was selected as a target by Inouye, the Japanese engineer in charge. Caron was shown a drawing of this by one of the retainers of the Roju or Shogun's Council who repeatedly urged upon him the importance of being ready to shoot by the 18th and of ensuring that at least one of the bombs might fall in the houses. On the 20th June the Hollanders were warned to be ready early next morning, and accordingly before sunrise on the 21st, they proceeded to the firing-range accompanied by two regents of the daimyo of Hirado. Here they found many soldiers, and were subsequently joined by three members of the Roju, the engineer Inouye and other Japanese gunners and officials, all of whom had been ordered to attend by the Shogun[1]. The mortars were already placed on beddings of two layers of planks nailed together, and were greatly admired by the assembled notables. After the Hollanders had been entertained with food and drink in a nearby temple, the party proceeded back to the range, where the mortars were loaded; this gave the Japanese another surprise, for they were astonished to see that a round-shot of 12 inches diameter, weighing over 56 catties, could be fired by a charge of only about $7^1/_2$ catties of gun-

---

[1] The three members of the Roju, or Shogun's Council, who were present on this occasion were: — Hotta Masamori, Kaga no-kami, daimyo of Sakura; Abe Shigetsugu Tsushima-no kami, dainmyo of Iwatsuki; Nobunari Makino, Takumi-no-kami. The two first-named were amongst Iemitsu's most trusted councillors, and followed him to "the yellow streams" on his death in 1651. Over Takumi-no-kami, and the engineer Inouye cf. *infra*. The names of those present are taken from the short account in the *Tokugawa Jikki*.

powder. What followed is best told in Caron's own words.
"The mortars being laden, all the gentlemen went in their
tent aside, and told us to open fire. The first shot fell too
short, yet was observed to fall into a deep marshy hollow
wherein rice was planted, between 17 and 18 feet deep, and
consequently in their opinion it was either lost, or could not
possibly take effect; albeit it proved to be the contrary, for
shortly afterwards it burst with such violence that all the mud,
slime and filth was hurled so high into the air, that all who
saw it were astonished, and particularly the regents who
could not show enough amazement. At the second shot, the
bomb exploded in the mortar, whereby the gunner's face was
severely burned and all the rest of us were wounded more or
less, whilst the planks and hanging curtains round the firing-
point were all torn asunder and smashed to pieces. The gentlemen at once came running up to see what had happened, and
found most of our men covered with blood, especially the
gunner, Christian, whom we caused to be carried to the
lodging as soon as possible. Owing to this mishap, we thought
that they would tell us to stop, but on the contrary they urged
us to take courage, (which anyway we did not lack), saying
that such accidents could easily happen when similar ex-
periments were being performed, wherefore we should not
give it up but rather go on, although they asked his Honour
the President if he would not join them in their tent and
watch the firing from there, so that if a similar accident should
occur, his Honour would remain unharmed. Accordingly
after everybody had washed, cleaned and dressed his hurts,
the work was pushed on rapidly, whilst Hans Woolf, gunner
of the yacht *Bredam*, who had cast the mortars, courageously
took charge, albeit he had likewise been injured in the first
explosion. The third shot was fired, and fell nicely in the
direction of the houses, although again rather short, into the
rice field, wherein, as it was very loose earth, it made a hole of
9 feet in diameter and between 5 and 6 feet deep, whereat
their Worships were also greatly amazed. At the fourth shot,
the bomb again burst in the same mortar in which the other
had also exploded, wherefore it was presumed that the reason
was because this mortar was something smaller than the
other one of the pair, and we therefore gave up this mortar

and thenceforward shot with one mortar; on this discharge, likewise, the surrounding planks and fence were smashed in the same way as formerly, but nobody was hurt. The fifth shot was fired by the small mortar, and the bomb burst in mid-air, looking like a flash of lightning in a very curious way, whereat they likewise wondered; yet the councillors asked each other what it meant, whereon the councillor Taecke-mondono [1], our friend, at once replied that although this was not the usual practice, yet it was done this once in order to make them laugh [sic]. The 6, 7, 8, 9, 10 and 11th shots were likewise fired, and all fell round about the target or houses made for that purpose, including the 6th shot which was only $8^1/_2$ feet away from the houses; they all had great effect, to the no little amazement of those who saw it, which so greatly encouraged their Worships that they had scarcely any patience left to wait, saying that altho' none of these shots had hit the target, yet the result was satisfactory, for if they had fallen in a castle then they would have done great hurt and damage, wherefore we could now stop, yet they wanted to see what would have happened if a bomb had fallen in one of the houses; they therefore told us to place a bomb in one of the houses, and light the fuse to see what would happen. This was accordingly done, and the bomb burst into pieces with a tremendous roar, and in a twinkling the flames had seized hold of the roof (which was thatched with straw, and built of light wood) as fiercely as if the whole thing had been ablaze for some time, whereupon they clapped their hands in delight and were so pleased that they all went together to see the fire, telling us not to shoot any more, as they had seen sufficient and were fully satisfied.

The aforesaid gentlemen, on reaching the burning house, and on seeing the huge holes made by the bombs in the earth, had all they could do to express their amazement, and to praise the mortars, excepting the engineer Inouye-dono who took no regard of all this business, and kept silent, — the reason being that he, who had made and practised many inventions, thought that his prestige would be diminished by this great work [2]. Being troubled over this, he was addressed by the

---

[1] i.e. Nobunari Makino, Takumi-no-kami.
[2] This Inouye was a *teppo-gata* or official who directed the manufacture of mus-

commissioner (or spies[1] as they are called) as follows:
— "Inouye dono! you say nothing about this work; praise
these things if you are just; praise them, for they are indeed
praiseworthy!" whereupon the engineer was fairly shamed,
and made excuses, subsequently praising the mortars, albeit
insincerely. The day before, the Governor had issued a decree
that nobody should come and watch; this was carried out as
far as the immediate neighbourhood of the target and firing-
place was concerned, but the surrounding plain and hills were
covered with an enormous multitude of people [2]. All the
bombs, however far from each other, at whatever distance
from the house-targets, however wide or deep they had fallen
were immediately dug up and sketched by surveyors and
painters, in order to show to His Majesty. Meanwhile the
mortars and appurtenances were all packed into separate
cases again, and carried to the ammunition-magazine in the
castle, by about 300 men. Finally, after their Worships had
again entertained us with wine and a banquet, they gave us a
friendly farewell, and so returned to the Castle and we to our
lodging. From there we went to the lord of Hirado's house,
where we again told His Excellency about everything, whilst
he had already been informed of it in detail by his regents
who had been with us continuously; he was delighted thereat, wished us good-luck, and so we parted after a good
reception."

On the 22nd and 23rd June, the Hollanders were kept busy
interviewing members of the Roju about the mortars, and
hearing about the Shogun Iemitsu's pleasure with their performance. Caron was informed that although this year twelve
richly-laden Dutch ships had taken away much treasure out
of the country, yet the Shogun considered himself more than
repaid with the mortars. The Hollanders also gave demonstrations, in the house of one of the councillors, of the con-

kets and cannon, and who instructed others in their use. This office was hereditary
in the Inouye and Tatsuke families in Tokugawa days. (Papinot's *Dictionary*, p. 651)

[1] *Dwarskijckers* in the original. *Metsuke* was the Japanese term for these officials.
This particular official was named Kanematsu Yagoyemon Masanao according to the
Tokugawa Jikki.

[2] The scene of the trial was in Azabu, according to the *Tokugawa Jikki*. According
to the same authority the range from the mortars to the targets was about 4 cho, (i.e.
about 450 yards or 430 metres).

PLATE II   P. 34

Mortar cast at Hirado and inscribed *Hans Wolfgang Braun von Ulm me fecit Firando 1639*

struction and use of quadrants, filling bombs, lighting fuses and so forth. That the gratitude of the Japanese was not limited to mere words was shown on the 25th of June, when the daimyo of Hirado was summoned to the palace by three members of the Roju, who told him in the Shogun's name, as follows: —

1. *Owing to my indisposition I have not been able to receive in audience the Captain of the Hollanders who has come to render me homage, and to offer me presents on behalf of his Masters. He must not take this to heart, as only my sickness has prevented this.*

2. *Three years ago, the same Captain presented me with a magnificent candelabrum, with which I was well pleased*[1]. *And now that he has brought this marvellous cannon, which affords us the greatest pleasure, in order to recompense him for his trouble, I give to him (which does not ordinarily happen) 200 taels of silver, and grant him permission to depart, wishing him a lucky journey back to his business-place.*

Furthermore, the Shogun told the daimyo of Hirado, through the Roju, as follows: —

1. *The Hollanders who trade in your domain, have presented me with a wonderful and extraordinary cannon through their Chief, which may be regarded as one of the country's jewels, and forasmuch as these emanate from your domain, I hereby acknowledge my appreciation of the fact that it was done in my service and to my honour.*

2. *After this I will issue orders that more such cannon are to be cast, and you will therefore take good heed that nobody may see or talk about the making thereof.*

On receipt of these instructions, the daimyo of Hirado thanked the Shogun through the Roju for his favours to himself and to the Hollanders, and informed the latter of their contents. In addition to Caron's reward of 200 taels of silver, the gunner Christiaen, and Hans Wolfgang who had cast the mortars, each received 25[2]. On the 26th, Caron received another 30 taels of silver and some other presents from various

[1] This Candelabrum is still to be seen at Ieyasu's mausoleum in Nikko, where it was placed in 1636. Cf. Hagenaer's *Reise* on p. 91 of the *Begin ende Voortgangh*, 1645.

[2] One of these 3 mortars cast by Hans Wolfgang in 1639 at Hirado, is now in the Military Museum, Kudan, Tokyo. For a biographical sketch of Hans Wolfgang's interesting career see p. xlix of my edition of *A True Description* ... *op. cit.*

members of the Roju, the rest of the day being spent in preparations for the return journey which commenced on the
next day; Osaka was reached on the 7th of July and Hirado
on the 13th, after a quick journey favoured by good weather.

In accordance with his instructions, Caron started to cast
some mortars for the Shogun very soon after his return to
Hirado. One of the gunners who was useful in this connection
was a certain Laurens Bartolszoon of Bergen in Norway,
who had previously been reduced to that rank from the position of boatswain on account of his bad conduct; owing to his
usefulness in casting the mortars, he was pardoned by Caron,
and placed as quartermaster on board of the ship *Engel*, which
under the command of Abel Jansz. Tasman was then (October 1639) on a voyage in Japanese waters in search of the
fabled gold and silver islands [1].

These mortars took nearly a year to make and they were
not finished until July 1640, there being seven of them in all,
which together with their appurtenances had cost 820 taels [2].
As Caron had already left for the court in April, these
mortars were not (apparently) transported to Yedo that year.
However, Caron had taken some gunners and a "fire-worker"
with him and these gave exhibitions of bombs, grenades,
fire-balls and similar things to various grandees. One of the
demonstrations nearly had a fatal result. The councillor Nobunari Makino [3] was a particular enthusiast for these things,
and one fine day in June he invited Caron and the gunner to
come to his house and make fireballs, etc., which was accordingly done, whilst "his highness followed everything with
the closest attention and witnessed the work in no little
amazement, but, as evening came on, he told the gunner to
postpone the work till the following day, and to stay that night
as his guest, which he did, being bountifully entertained with
all kinds of food and drink. The next day the gunner re-
commenced his business (albeit in the absence of the honble
Mr. Caron, as he been excused by His Highness, who had

---

[1] Leupe *Reize van Maarten Gerritsz. Vries in 1643 naar het noorden en oosten van Japan*, etc. (Amsterdam, 1858).

[2] *Dagh-Register Batavia Anno 1640*, p. 139. Caron advised that the Japanese should not be charged anything for them; a sprat to catch a whale.

[3] Takumi-no-kami; hence his appearance in the Dutch records under the name or Taeckemondono.

told him that he would be detained all day at court), but on his trying to drive an iron nail into the ball, the end of it struck against the cast-iron grenade inside, which gave off sparks and thus exploded the ball with the filled grenade, with such force that all those who were standing in the hall looking on, were thrown violently on the ground, whilst the gunner and several servants of the councillor who were helping him had their faces, foreheads and feet blown away, and the dwelling, which had just been finished building, together with all the precious carved wood-work and other rarities, smashed and broken to pieces; the fire finally reached a balcony, which caused no little alarm, but fortunately with the help of God it was extinguished by a mass of people. The lord Taeckenmondono received these tidings in the castle, and seemed more pleased than sorry thereat; partly because the sound of the explosion had not been heard in the castle owing to the noise made by the workmen who were laying the foundations of a new palace therein, and secondly because he had not lost his house, which was 40 roods wide by 50 roods long and superbly built, but chiefly because the fire had not spread to the castle, just behind which his house was situated The honble Mr. Caron, hearing of this mishap, at once hastened thither to make excuses for the accident, being very much afraid that something bad would come of it, but contrary to all expectation he was very friendly received by the aforesaid lord and his sons, who even consoled him in his affliction, saying that nobody in the world could prevent such accidents occurring; he intended to hold a big feast with his family and relations that evening, since he had now realised what a lucky person he was and that no harm could befall him, as had been made clear that day. The damage was estimated at fully 3,000 taels" [1].

Besides the unfortunate fireworker's grenades, Caron had also taken with him to Yedo, two bronze field guns with their carriages and gear, as a present for the Shogun.

This year of 1640 sounded the death-knell of the Portuguese intercourse with Japan, as was proved in the most gruesome fashion when 61 out of 74 members of a Lusitanian mission from Macau were beheaded at Nagasaki on the order

Dagh-Register gehouden in 't Casteel Batavia, Anno 1640–1641, pp. 134–5.

of the Shogun. A similar tragedy at Hirado was only averted by the coolness of François Caron with his twenty years' continuous experience of Japan, and by the Shogun's delight with the mortars, for "experience has taught us that when it rains on the Portuguese, the Company likewise gets wet from the drops", as Caron wrote to the Governor-General Van Diemen. Withal, Caron told his superiors that the mortars ought to be cast in Europe for the future, and not in Japan, whilst he urged the importance of sending some as a present to Baba Saburozavemon, the Bugyo of Nagasaki, "not doubting but that the same will have an extraordinary good effect" [1].

Numerous other grandees asked for presents of firearms, amongst them the Shogun's uncle, Tokugawa Yorinobu, daimyo of Kii, and the commissioner Inouye Chikugo-no-Kami, chief inquisitor of Japan, who required two pairs of small pistols, some muskets and hand grenades. The sudden curtailment of the Hollanders' trade at Hirado, and their forced removal to the narrow confines of Deshima in Nagasaki in May 1641 had, however, apparently temporarily cooled the Company's ardour in ministering to the whims of the Bakufu officials, as the following extract from a letter of Pieter Antoniszoon Overtwater, who had been *opperhofd* or chief of the Dutch factory in 1645, will show: [2]

"During our stay in Japan, we have had many requests for a mortar-gunner; firstly and mainly in Yedo from the four chiefest councillors of the realm, on the very day of our audience, and shortly afterwards in the court, in the very next room to the one wherein we had rendered obeisance to His Majesty, and subsequently in Nagasaki from the Governors on numerous occasions. We tried to smooth it over with polite excuses, and thereafter the matter was dropped.

I am of the opinion that we should not trouble ourselves

[1] *Idem*, p. 149. As a result of this, the Government at Batavia wrote to the Directors in Holland for some special "gunners and fireworkers" to be sent out to the East. MacLeod, *op. cit.* II, p. 301.

[2] Written from Castle Zeelandia in Taiwan 31. i. 1646. (Hague Archives, *overgecomen brieue Boek* II. v. folios 682–686). Pieter Anthoniszoon arrived in India from Holland in 1640. In 1641 he was *fiscaal* in Taiwan, and in 1642-3, and again in 1644-5 *opperhoofd* in Japan. From 1646–1650 he was Vice-Governor of Taiwan, returning to Holland in that year. In 1663 he came back to the Indies, and died at Batavia in 1681. (Cf. note (2) on p. 554 of Dr. Stapel's edition of Van Dam's *Beschrijvinge van de O.I. Compagnie*. The Hague 1931).

greatly as to whether the mortar-gunner comes very speedily within the next two years or not. These mortars are great jewels, and one may well ask whether it had not been wiser never to have taught this proud and haughty nation about them; but that being now past, we must resign ourselves thereto, and act as the present circumstances demand. We ought to be rather evasive, and fob them off with polite nothings like they do us. If it is a new *opperhofd* who is asked about it, then he can declare that he neither knows nor has heard tell of any mortar-gunner; if it falls to my share, then must I say that I've been in Taiwan, or that I could not speak personally with their Honours, or that the Heer General is dead, or that their Honours have enough work to do as it is, or that the mortar-gunner is dead, or that he had a cantankerous disposition which rendered him unfit to associate with Japanese, or some other trumped-up pretexts. They may then begin to think, as is the truth, that we are not so very eager to do exactly what they tell us, and that these are but vain and frivolous excuses, but that is no matter, neither can the Company suffer anything thereby. They may grumble and mutter to themselves, but that is all the same to us, and we must meet them more than half way with outward courtesies; the fairmindedness on which they pride themselves (and not wholly without reason), will not permit them to ill-treat us on that account. We are in good favour at court, and provided that we obey and fulfill the orders and commands which His Majesty lays upon us, our affairs will remain on a firm and secure basis. If the mortar-gunner does not come next year, I am of opinion that there will be no further enquiries for one, and we can then send one, two or three years later, with many excuses for the long delay; if he is still welcome, then everything will be all right, or if they have lost the desire for one, then we shall have saved ourselves much trouble and expense: for they never consider this even in the busiest time of the trade, being quite capable of stopping all transactions for a time, just on account of the mortar-gunner, if they felt so inclined. There was one here four years ago, of whom they never took the slightest notice; they likewise must learn to open their mouths wide when porridge is offered [1], and what

---

[1] "Sij moeten alsmede leren gapen alsser pap geboden wort."

did it help the Company in the year '40, that a mortar-gunner had been up at Court in the year '39? [Here Overtwater is wrong. The mortars cast at Hirado in 1639 formed one of the reasons why the Hollanders were not expelled in 1640]. At the end of our *Journal* we have noted how we had spoken to the Governors (of Nagasaki) about the sojourn of some of our people on the island, the early commencement of the trading season, and permission to export copper. Should it come to pass that they consent to all these things in general, or to the last of the three in particular, then they will have earned their mortar-gunner being sent them once next year, as these demands have now come to their knowledge; but otherwise I think, under correction, that it will be better to let them wait awhile and think over our requests once more, or if they should not do so, that we should not be so complaisant towards them as otherwise, without, however, letting any-thing thereof be seen in the very least, because otherwise they would banish and bundle us out of the country neck and crop."

This forceful advice was apparently taken, for no mortar-gunner was sent to Nippon until 1649. In that year, however, the Company had perforce to send a special mission to Japan to thank the Shogun for his clemency in releasing some Dutch sailors who had made an unauthorized landing at Nambu on the N.E. coast of Japan in 1643 [1], and to explain away the ten years' truce concluded with the hated Portuguese in 1644. In the instructions for the Ambassador, which were drawn up by Caron, then Director-General at Batavia, it was expressly stated that "the Emperor had on many occasions demanded that a mortar-gunner should be sent, but this had hitherto been prevented owing to pressing preoccupations; but you are now to state you have brought with you a man skilled in that art." This gunner was Juriaan Schaedel, who with three other Hollanders remained in Yedo for nearly six months teaching the Japanese about "fireworks", after the envoy and the rest of the mission had left in April 1650.

---

[1] These men were from the *Castricum* and *Breskens* which, under the command of Maarten Gerritsz Vries, were making a voyage of discovery in the direction of Yezo and East Tartary. Full details of the sojourn of the party in Japan will be found in Montanus: *"Gedenkwaerdige Gesantschappen ... aan de Kaisaren van Japan,"* pp. 290–355, and Nachod: *Beziehungen* p. 306–315. The castaways included three or four gunners, but the Japanese made no use of them.

In 1646, the surveyor and cartographer, Hojo Ujinaga, alluded to elsewhere, visited Nagasaki in his capacity as an official inspector of firearms for the Bakufu, and was there taught *inter alia* how to blow a trumpet by one of the ship's trumpeters [1]. Four years later Ujinaga received more professional instruction in the art of gunnery from Juriaan Schaedel, who was the gunner left behind by Frisius' mission to the Shogun's court at Yedo as previously mentioned. Other acounts speak of Ujinaga having been taught survey by Schaedel's companion, the doctor Caspar Schambergen, who is credited with so much in Japan besides the introduction of a new school of medicine. Obviously however it was Schaedel rather than Schambergen who was competent to impart such instruction; and this is the more likely since we know that Ujinaga was taught something about Dutch methods of siege warfare at this time, concerning which he has left extant a treatise entitled *Oranda Kojoden* [2].

In this same year of 1650, the Dutch also carried out some field-firing practice near Yedo with a field gun presented to the Shogun by Frisius' mission, Hojo Ujinaga being present amongst many others; but subsequently there seems to have been a distinct cooling in the ardour of the Japanese for studying Western methods of gunnery, as the memory of the Shimabara rebellion receded into the distant past. The long peace of the Yedo period had its inevitable effect of a weakening of military enthusiasm, and records of the presentation of cannon by the Hollanders become few and far between. The efforts of the eighth Shogun, Yoshimune, to restore the martial spirit of the samurai by encouraging military arts, do not seem to have extended to such technical sciences as gunnery, though there are a few entries in the Japanese records of his time which may betoken a renewed if somewhat tepid interest [3]. The real revival of interest in European military matters came into being, like the other aspects of Western learning, in the last quarter of the XVIIIth century, and is evidenced in such works as Hayashi Shihei's

[1] *Shinsen Yogaku Nempyo*, p. 13.

[2] *Shinsen Yogaku Nempyo*. p. 14. Itazawa, *Rangaku no Igi, etc.* Part II, pp. 164–5, where an extract of Ujinaga's treatise on Dutch methods of siege warfare is given. Cf. also MacLeod, *op. cit.*, p. 369.

[3] *Shinsen Yogaku Nempyo*. pp. 32, 42, 43.

classic *Kaikoku Heidan* (military tales of a sea-girt country). The intrusion of the English frigate *Phaeton* into the harbour of Nagasaki in 1808, together with the inadequacy and incompetence prevailing in the local coast defence arrangements which this untoward incident revealed, seem also to have given a temporary spurt to the study of European gunnery and of Dutch books on this science, to judge by entries in contemporary Japanese records [1]. As the Bakufu regime drew to its close and the stormy years preceding the Meiji Restoration were ushered in, there was naturally a vast increase in the number of translations of Dutch books on artillery and the allied arms which were circulated both in print and in manuscript throughout Japan, but these do not fall within the scope of this essay [2].

Although amongst the European military arts it was principally gunnery in which the Japanese were interested, from time to time they displayed a fitful interest in other branches of the "noble Art Military." From the records of the early Dutch and English traders at Hirado, we learn that plans, pictures and paintings of battles, both by land and sea, commanded a ready sale in Japan, whilst the presentation of two contemporary plans of the sieges of Hertzogenbosch and La Rochelle, has already been mentioned. In 1634, a complete set of model lead soldiers representing a European army in battle array (such as were used by Princes Maurice and Frederik Hendrik in planning their campaigns), was destined as a special present to the Shogun Iemitsu and brought over by a Captain David de Polamme, though I can find no record of their actual presentation [3].

The lessons in horse mastership and stable management given by Corporal Hans Jurgen Keyserling of Hamburg at Yedo in 1729–30, and again in 1734, on the initiative of Shogun Yoshimune are worth a passing mention if nothing more [4].

---

[1] A graphic description of the *Phaeton* incident is printed in Vol. III of Murdoch's *History*. Doeff also has an account in his *Herinneringen*. As a result of this incident, the Dutch interpreters at Nagasaki received orders to learn gunnery, whilst Dutch works on fortification and coast defence were translated by Motogi and Otsuki Gentaku. (*Shinsen Yogaku Nempyo*, pp. 93–4).

[2] A list of such works will be found in Araki's Catalogue pp. 158–173, and in the *Shinsen Yogaku Nempyo*, *passim*.

[3] Letter of G.G. Van Diemen & his Council, 24. v. 1634.

[4] Some details will be found in pp. 247–8 of Feenstra Kuiper's *Japan en de Buiten-*

After the death of Yoshimune the newly-awakened interest both in the martial arts as in things European, again relapsed into the complacent stagnation of the previous decades, until the renewed interest in Dutch scholarship from c. 1771 onwards. In 1790 a work called *Oranda Chikujosho* (Treatise on the Dutch art of fortification) was compiled by the famous *Rangakusha* Maeno Ryotaku, but it does not appear to have been published. [1] The study of Western drill and tactics also seems to have commenced in real earnest about this time. The present writer possesses a copy of the *Reglement op de Exercitien en evolution van de Infanterie van den Staat*, printed at the Hague in 1771, which bears the seal of one of the famous Narabayashi family of interpreters, — perhaps Titsingh's friend and mentor, Narabayashi Jubei. In comparison with works on medicine or geography, interest in such matters remained comparatively slight until about the Tempo period, when there began a regular spate of copies, translations and adaptations of European (principally Dutch) military manuals and text-books on all aspects of the science of war [2].

Of books on military subjects revealing Western influence before 1810, the following two may be mentioned.

1. *Kaikoku Heidan*. 3 vols. in-4to. Published at Yedo in Kwansei 3 (1791).

The blocks of this work, together with those of the *Sankoku Tsuran* by the same author, were destroyed in the following year, and its circulation prohibited.

2. *Seiyo-kako Shinki*. 2 vols. in -4to. Published at Osaka, Kyoto and Yedo in Kyowa 2 (1802). This was derived from a seventeenth-century Sino-Jesuit translation of L. Collado's *Pratica Manuale di Artiglieria*, (Venice, 1586).

wereld in de XVIIIe eeuw. ('s-Gravenhage, 1921). Japanese accounts in the *Shinsen Yogaku Nempyo*, pp. 42–47. A contemporary *makimono* representing Keyserling imparting instruction to the Shogunal retainers is preserved in the Imperial Household Museum at Ueno. Cf. also Krieger *op. cit.* pp. 21–25 and 28–9.

[1] *Shinsen Yogaku Nempyo*, p. 75.

[2] Araki's Catalogue pp. 158–173 contains the titles of scores of such works.

[3] *Early European Military Influence in Japan*, p. 36, and *Rin Shihei and his Picture of a Dutch East-India ship*, pp. 53–8. (In *Trans. As. Soc. Japan*, 1932–3). The latest study in this field which has come my way is that of Delmer M. Brown, *The impact of firearms on Japanese warfare, 1543–98* in *The Far Eastern Quarterly*, Vol. VII, pp. 236–253, (May, 1948). In his well-documented study, Professor Brown credits the introduction of European firearms with more far-reaching economic, social and political implications than I have been willing to allow.

III. MEDICINE, BOTANY AND ASTRONOMY

a) *Medicine and Surgery*. The study and practice of Western medicine and surgery in Japan dates from the time of the Portuguese, and its first exponents were the XVIth century Jesuit missionaries some of whom, as for instance Father Luis d'Almeida, achieved considerable fame in this connection. This style of medicine was known as *Namban-ryu* or the School of the Southern Barbarians, in contradistinction to the more widely spread native methods which were modelled on the centuries-old Chinese practice. Amongst the leading schools of *Namban* origin may be cited the Kurizaki school founded by Kurizaki Dozen, and the Yoshida school founded by Yoshida Jikyu.

With the arrival of the Hollanders in Japan, the native physicians, or some of them, began to turn their attention to learning their art from the Dutchmen, and this practice was facilitated by the removal of the Dutch factory from Hirado to Deshima in 1641. Whether the theories taught by the Hollanders were radically different from those propounded by the Portuguese missionaries may be doubted, though they were probably more up to date as the study of medical science in the Netherlands stood on a relatively high plane during the XVIIth century. At any rate, the schools deriving from Dutch origin were termed *Oranda*-(Holland) or *Komo* (Red -hair)-*ryu* to distinguish them from those of *Namban* (Portuguese) or of Chinese origin [1].

[1] The best European sources for the study of the influence of Dutch medicine in Japan are Kleiweg de Zwaan, *Völkerkundliches und Geschichtliches über die Heilkunde der Chineser und Japaner mit besonderer Berücksichtigung Holländischer Einflüsse* (Haarlem, 1917), and pp. 259–266 of Feenstra Kuiper's *Japan en de Buitenwereld in de XVIIIe eeuw*. For the Japanese side, I have chiefly relied on Professor Ozawa's *Igaku chushin no Nichi-Ran Kohoshi* (*Ninsei Chiri*, Vol. I, Part 4, 1933) and Professor T. Itazawa's *Rangaku no Igi* etc. op. cit. Compare also, Whitney, *Notes on the history of medical progress in Japan* (*Trans. As. Soc. Japan*, Vol. XII, Yokohama, 1885) pp. 303–44. S. Kure, *Einfluss der fremden, insbesondere der deutschen Medizin auf die Japanische vom anfang des 18. bis gegen das Ende des 19. Jahrhunderts* (in *Jubiläumsband* of the O.A.C. Tokyo, Vol. I, pp. 76–91 (Tokyo, 1933).

The first landmark in the history of the study of Dutch medicine in Japan is the visit of the physician Caspar Schambergen to Nagasaki and Yedo in 1650, as a member of the suite of Blockhovius' and Frisius' mission from Batavia in the previous year. Schambergen remained for some months in Yedo after the return of Frisius to Nagasaki, and is credited with a good deal of activity in teaching not only the elements of his profession but those of gunnery and survey as well. Exactly how far his instruction extended it is difficult to say, but he gave his name to a school of surgery — *Caspar-ryu* — which lasted down to the end of the Tokugawa period. Amongst his pupils may be mentioned Kawaguchi Ryoan and Inomata Denbei, the most celebrated exponent of the Caspar School being Irako Dochu. A manuscript entitled *Komo Gekwa* (Redhair surgery) whose origin was attributed to the teachings of Schambergen, was exhibited by its owner, Dr. Fujikawa, at the Japanese Exhibition of Medical History in March 1930.

During the next few decades quite a number of Japanese physicians and doctors visited Nagasaki to learn a smattering of Western medicinal and surgical methods from the Dutch resident surgeon at Deshima; whilst not a few of the interpreters specialised in the same branches of study, either as a side-line of their own choosing, or by order of the Shogunate. Amongst these last may be mentioned Narabayashi Shingobei (Chinzan) [1], Katsuragawa Hochiku, and Yoshio Kosaku, all of whom founded the schools of surgery bearing their names during the second half of the XVIIth century. Several daimyo also sent their retainers to Nagasaki for personal instruction at the hands of either the Dutch surgeons or of Nagasaki interpreters, it being customary for them to be granted certificates of proficiency by the former before returning to their fiefs. One such document dating from 1665 has been jealously preserved in the family of the original recipient at Hirado to this day, and although it has been reproduced in recent Japanese works, may be quoted again here as these are difficult of access in Europe [2]. The document in

[1] A page of whose *Koi Gekwa Soden* (Surgery as taught by Red-hair Barbarians) is reproduced on Plate 63 of T. Nagayama's *Taigai Shiryo Bijitsu Daikwan*, (Nagasaki, 1918). Cf. also Krieger, *op. cit.*, pp. 4–5.

[2] i.e. Plate 9 of T. Nagayama's *Taigai Shiryo* etc. *op. cit.*, and Professor S. Koda's article on this document on pp. 215–219 of his *Oranda Zatsuwa* (Tokyo, 1934).

question relates to one Arashiyama Hoan, a retainer of the daimyo of Hirado, who studied Western methods of surgery at Nagasaki for three years before being awarded a certificate of proficiency by Daniel Busch, the surgeon at Deshima in 1665, as is apparent from the translation of the original,

We the undersigned bear witness and attest as the truth that the Japanese named Choan, servant of the lord of Hirado, has studied for a considerable time under the Dutch surgeons, and is well instructed (so far as we can tell) in the art of surgery. He is therefore well acquainted with the potency of Dutch medicines, of which he has given us sufficient practical proofs, and we hereby declare him to be an accomplished practitioner.

Japan, in the agency at Nagasaki, this 21st. January, 1665.

> (signed) Jacob Gruijs, 1665.
> Nicolaes de Roy,
> D. Busch, surgeon on the
> island of Deshima.

One of the better known works was the Netherlands translation of the famous French surgeon, Ambrose Paré's (1510–1590) work, published at Amsterdam in 1649, and which formed the basis of Narabayashi Chinzan's *Koi Gekwa Soden* already quoted. No doubt other medical books were imported by the Hollanders, and we know from the accounts of visiting physicians such as Kaempfer or Thunberg, as well as from the journals of the *opperhoofden* themselves, that it was usually the surgeon rather than the *opperhoofd* who was the centre of attraction during the visit of the annual Dutch mission to the court at Yedo. This was clearly on account of his supposedly superior scientific attainments, but unfortunately these were by no means of an invariably high order and frequently the surgeons were little better than horse-leeches. This was particularly the case during the first half of the eighteenth century, and even when men of exceptional merit were dispatched from Batavia such as Andreas Cleyer or Ten Rhyne, the language bar formed a great obstacle to the ready diffusion of their knowledge as Feenstra Kuiper has pointed out. In despite of the yearly interrogation of the Dutch surgeons at court and the importation of medical books and stores throughout the eighteenth century, matters remained therefore more or less where they were in Kaempfer's time until the publication of the *Kaitai Shinsho* in 1774.

The story of the origin of this book, the first really scientific work of the West to be circulated in Japan, has often been told, and need only be mentioned here in its simplest form. According to the generally accepted accounts as recorded by Sugita Gempaku in his *Rangaku koto hajime* (Beginning of Dutch Studies), he and a fellow *Rangakusha* or Dutch scholar, Maeno Ryotaku, bribed an *Eta* or outcast executioner to let them see the dismembered corpse of an old woman, nicknamed Aocha Baba or "Old Mother Green-tea", on the Kotsugahara execution ground at Yedo in the eighth year of Meiwa (1771). Comparing the arrangement of the viscera and bones in the body with that shown in a Dutch edition of the Anatomical Tables of Johan Adam Kulmus of Breslau which one of them happened to possess, they were struck by the accuracy of the European representations as opposed to the generally accepted Chinese notions [1]. On their homeward way they agreed to translate it, which they eventually did with the help of some like-minded enthusiasts, in face of the difficulties graphically — if somewhat exaggeratedly — described by Sugita in his auto-biography. The importance of this work has been somewhat overestimated by various writers, and not least by Sugita Gempaku himself, but withal it does constitute a definite landmark in the history of the progress of Western science in Japan. Dismemberments of corpses had of course been carried out in Japan before, and Sugita with his companions was not breaking such new ground as he believed, either in medical science or in the study of the Dutch language, in both of which respects some of the Nagasaki interpreters were a long way ahead of him despite all his assertions to the contrary.

Nevertheless it was the first time that the general correctness of European as opposed to Sino-Japanese anatomical theories had been demonstrated publicly in print, and the translation of the Dutch original in the short space of two years

---

[1] *Japan en de Buitenwereld*, p. 262. Whitney, *Notes*, p. 328. A. German translation of the *Rangaku Kotohajime*, by Dr. K. Mori will be found in the Tokyo Jesuit review *Monumenta Nipponica*. Vol. V, pp. 144–166 and 501–522 (Tokyo, 1942).

by Sugita and his comrades with their limited qualifications, was certainly a *tour-de-force* which commands our
respect. The book made a great sensation on its first appearance and was very soon sold out. A copy was presented
to the Shogun, and examples of the original edition are now
very hard to come by. It is certainly curious that neither
Thunberg nor Titsingh, who were in Japan a few years after
the publication of this work, make mention either of it or of
its authors, but perhaps even by that time copies were practically unprocurable.

    1. *Kaitai Shinsho* by Sugita Gempaku. 5 vols. 4to.
       printed at Yedo in Annei 3 (1774).

    This work was edited by Sugita Gempaku (1733–1818),
Nakagawa Junan (1739–1780), Ishikawa Genjo (1744–1816)
and Katsuragawa Hoshu (1751–1809) under the super-
intendence of the celebrated *Rangakusha*, Maeno Ryotaku
(1723–1803). Strictly speaking, this work is not based solely
on Kulmus' book of anatomical illustrations. The title-page,
with its Adam and Eve *motif*, is taken from that of Valverde's
Vivae Imagines partium corporis humani aereis formis expressae,
printed by Christopher Plantin at Antwerp in 1566 (reprinted 1579), or from the identical title-page in the Flemish
edition of 1568. Most of the anatomical illustrations which
follow are reproductions, with a few modifications, of those
in Johan Adam Kulmus' *Tabulae Anatomicae*, as published
in Gerard Dicten's Dutch translation of this work printed at
Amsterdam in 1734, under the title of *Ontleedkundige Tafe-
len*. The last four woodcuts in the *Kaitai Shinsho*, representing the tendons of the hands and feet, are not taken from
Kulmus' work, but from Godfried Bidloo's *Ontleding des
Menschelycken lichaams* (Amsterdam, 1690), or from the
Latin edition of this work printed five years earlier. All
these works ultimately derive from that of the famous six-
teenth-century Flemish surgeon, Vesalius, and the *Kaitai
Shinsho* may be fairly added to the already vast Vesalian
bibliography. Another and somewhat expanded edition of
the *Kaitai Shinsho* was published by Otsuki Gentaku in
1798, under the title of *Chotei Kaitai Shinsho*, and several
other editions were printed during the first half of the nineteenth century. Most of these were straightforward trans-

PLATE III   P. 48

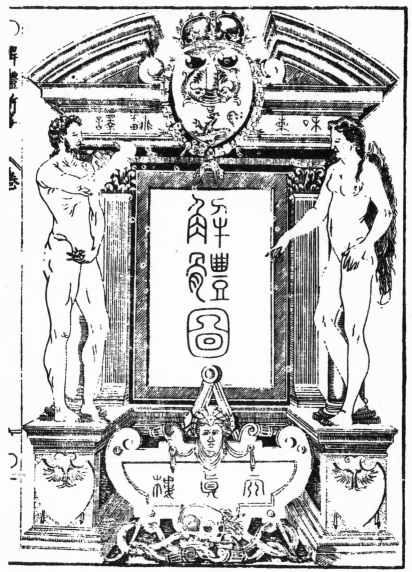

Title-page of the *Kaitai Shinsho*, 1774

PLATE IV

Title-page of the first Plantin edition of the Valverde-Vesalius *Anatomy,*
Antwerp, 1566

lations of Kulmus' work, and retained his frontispiece 1734 (depicting an anatomy theatre and table with surgical instruments), discarding the Plantin title-page of the 1566 Valverde-Vesalius, as well as the four woodcuts taken from Bidloo's book which Sugita Gempaku had inserted in his original edition [1].

2. *Yoi Shinsho* by Sugita Gempaku and Otsuki Genta-ku. Published in 1790.

Professor Kure states that this work (which, like those mentioned hereafter, I have not myself seen) was translated from a German surgical work by Laurens Heister, presumably through the intermediary of some Dutch version. In another place Professor Kure gives the date of the publication of this work as 1792. In any case it had a second edition in 1822.

3. *Seisetsu Naikwa Senyo* by Udagawa Gensui. Published in 1793.

Professor Kure states that this work was translated from a standard work on internal medicine by the Dutch physician Johannes de Gorter, and served as model for many subsequent works in Japanese. Udagawa Gensui (1755–1797) was the father of the more celebrated Udagawa Genshin (1769 –1834) who was the author — or rather translator-compiler – of the two following amongst many other similar works, —

4. *Ihan Teiko* by Udagawa Genshin. sm. 4to. 75 leaves. 3 books in 1 vol. Published at Yedo in Bunkwa 2 (1805). Second edition in Bunkwa 5 (1808).

This ,,Outline of Splanchnology" was the translation of a Dutch work on the visceral system.

5. *Oranda Kyokuho* by Udagawa Genshin; published in 1813.

This appears to be the earliest work dealing with European notions of pharmacology.

---

[1] The *Kaitai Shinsho* and its variants should be added to the numerous European works listed in Harvey Cushing's erudite and entertaining, *Bio-Bibliography of Andreas Vesalius* (New York, 1943). For the importance of Vesalius' work see Charles Singer and C. Rabin, *A Prelude to Modern Science. Being a discussion of the History sources and circumstances of the Tabulae Anatomicae Sex of Vesalius*, (Cambridge, 1946). For Kulmus and Bidloo's works cf. L. Choulant, *History and Bibliography of Anatomic Illustration*, (Chicago, 1920). For assistance in ferreting out the ultimate origins of the woodcuts in the *Kaitai Shinsho*, I am indebted to Mr. W. J. Bishop and his colleagues at the Wellcome Historical Medical Library, London, and to the Librarian of the Royal Library at The Hague.

6. *Gankwa Shinsho* by Sugita Ryukei; published in 1815. This book is of interest as being the earliest-known translation of a European work on ophthalmology and is apparently translated from the work of a certain v. Plenck.

b) *Botany, Zoology, and Chemistry*. In the sphere of natural history we have not much to add to the brief but comprehensive survey of Dr. Feenstra Kuiper on pp. 266–7 of his oft-quoted *Japan en de Buitenwereld in de achttiende eeuw*. As early as Kaempfer's time (1692) the Japanese displayed some interest in Western botany, and Kaempfer's own botanical excursions were made with the permission and approval of the Bakufu officials. Presents of strange animals had always been popular with the daimyo and Shogun from the time of the Portuguese who imported fine Arabian and Persian horses, besides tigers, deer and antelope as presents for Hideyoshi or his grandees. The Hollanders continued and expanded this custom, and from the third decade of the XVIIth century onwards, we have records of their importing (or being asked to procure) such varied animals as Persian and Frisian horses, bloodhounds, mastiffs, pheasants from Cape Verde, Siamese cranes and cassuaries from the East Indies.

On the occasion of the *opperhoofd* Johan Aouwer's mission to Yedo in 1717, the Shogun Yoshimune produced an old Dutch book on natural history about which he asked numerous questions. This book turned out to be a Dutch edition of the Polish naturalist John Johnstone's *Naeukeurige Beschrijving van de Natuur der Vier-Voetige Dieren, Vissen en Bloedloze Water Dieren, Vogelen, Kronkel-Dieren, Slangen en Draken*, Amsterdam 1660, which had been presented by the *opperhoofd* Hendrick Indijck in 1663. On the occasion of a subsequent mission to Yedo in 1731, the then *opperhoofd*, Jacob van der Waeijen, records in his Journal that this book was again produced at the Shogunal audience, and the Hollanders ordered to explain portions of it to the Shogun's physician through the intermediary of the chief interpreter Tosaburo. Johnstone was a Pole of Scots descent.

From the time of Yoshimune onwards, many doctors and physicians visited the Hollanders during their annual visit to

Yedo, when questions on natural history and allied sciences were the order of the day. As early as 1750 an extensive twelve volume compilation on European natural history had been composed by the Shogunal physicians from Dutch sources (apparently mainly derived from Johnstone's *magnum opus*), and this manuscript is still preserved in the Cabinet's Library at Tokyo.

A very popular source for the study of European botany in Japan was the works of the great botanist Dodonaeus, of which during the eighteenth century we have records of the importation of both the Leiden edition of 1608, and the Antwerp of 1644. Thunberg's stay in Japan was naturally not without influence on the study of botany by the native naturalists, and one of the most celebrated of them, Ito Keisuke, compiled a list of Japanese plants as classified by Thunberg (the *Taisei Honso Meiso*) a bibliographical description of which will be given *infra*. Botanical influence was not by any means one-sided. Thunberg identified a large number of Japanese plants, whilst Isaac Titsingh a few years later acquired numerous scrolls and books with paintings or woodcuts of zoological or botanical interest. Chief amongst these were two folio volumes containing 77 botanical drawings, which a French traveller who saw Titsingh's collection at Chinsura describes as follows: — "It was a present made to M. Titsingh by the wife of the chief physician, [Katsuragawa Hoshu] to the emperor. I doubt whether anything more perfect in its kind exists: the stalks, flowers, fruit, roots, all have the appearance of nature itself: opposite to each plant its name and properties are drawn rather than writen. The whole is the work of the Japanese lady by whom it was presented." Abel Rémusat in his account of Titsingh's Japanese collection, likewise writes of this botanical treatise in the most glowing terms, and laments that Titsingh's botanical manuscripts, which were much more complete and detailed than those of Thunberg, had not been edited and published by a competent European botanist [1].

It might be mentioned in passing that Japanese scholars (or some of them) referred to these sciences by their Latin names

---

[1] *Nouveaux Mélanges Asiatiques* I, p. 270–1. (Paris, 1829).

which they derived from the Hollanders, and which they transcribed by means of Sino-Japanese characters used phonetically. Thus zoologia, botanica, mineralogia, and physica were all transliterated in this way. This practice continued till about the early years of the Meiji period (c. 1870) when these terms were supplanted by their modern Japanese equivalents, *Dogaku, Kigaku, Sanbutsu no Gaku*, etc. [1].

The study of Western physics and natural philosophy did not begin in real earnest until the end of the XVIIIth century, Shidzuki Tadao's translation of Keill's *Inleiding tot een natuur- en wiskundige beschrijving des aardkloots* (Leyden, 1741) under the title of *Rekisho Shinsho* in 1798, marking the initial step in this connection. Subsequent works fall outside the scope of this article. As regards chemistry, called by Japanese scholars after the Latin term *chemica*, the first translation of a Dutch chemical work was not published till Tempo 8 (1837) so that the study of this science likewise falls outside the scope of this essay [2].

Amongst the pioneer works in the foregoing sciences we may find space for brief descriptions of the two following, although the second one does not, strictly speaking, come within the scope of this article from a chronological standpoint.

1 *Oranda Sanbutsu Zuko* by Fujimoto Yoshi. 5 vols. in-4to. Published at Kyoto in Kwansei 10 (1798).

Between the preface (dated Kwansei 9 or 1797) and the list of contents, is a sort of titlepage with a bastardized *Romaji* transcription of the Japanese title *San Bets Dsokoo* within a clock-face design surmounted by two inverted Ψ monograms of the Kamer Amsterdam. The work contains several woodcuts of birds and animals (ape, turkey, flying-fish, etc.) taken from Dutch books, besides many purely fanciful engravings, and the text is couched in anecdotal style. It is a purely popular work and of no scientific value. On quite a different plane is the

2. *Taisei Honso Meiso* by Ito Keisuke. 3 volumes in-4to. Published at Nagoya in Bunsei 12 (1829). Illustrated with 2 plates.

This work is rarely found when complete with the two

---

[1] Itazawa, *Rangaku no Igi*, etc. p. 25.
[2] *Ibidem*. p. 26. Cf. also Feenstra-Kuiper, *Japan en de Buitenwereld*, pp. 267, 270–1.

PLATE V   P. 52

長百卜喜乙勹荒

NAAMLYST
VAN
GEWASSEN
DOOR DEN BEROEMDEN
NATUURONDERZOEKER
C. P. THUNBERG, M. D.
OP JAPAN GEVONDEN.

HERZIEN EN MET JAPAN-
SCHE EN CHINEESCHE
NAMEN VERRYKT
DOOR
JTOO KEISKE.

TE NAGOJA,
By

BOENZY XI. (*1828.*)

品字祉叢書

Second title of Ito Keisuke's *Taisei Honso Meiso*, published at Nagoya in 1828

plates as follows, — (i) engraved portrait of C. P. Thunberg in the middle of Vol. I, copied from the portrait of the Swedish scholar which serves as a frontispiece to Langlé's French edition of his travels published at Paris in 1796 (English edition, London, 1798). (ii) cut of some 24 flowers on p. 32 of Vol. III. Most copies offered for sale lack one or both of these illustrations. On the *verso* of the portrait of Thunberg, is engraved the following legend, —

Naamlyst/ van/ Gewassen/ door den beroemden/ na-tuuronderzoeker/ C. P. Thunberg, M. D./ op Japan ge-vonden./ Herzien en met Japan- / sche en Chineesche/ namen verrykt/ door/ ITOO KEISKE/ —/ Te Nagoja,/ By [1] (blank)/ BOENZY XI. (See reproduction, Plate V).

c) *Astronomy.* Interest in European astronomy dates from the earliest times of Japan's contact with the West, and it was the astronomical knowledge of St. Francisco Xavier S.J. and other Jesuits which was largely responsible for their early rapid success. Even towards the end of the so-called "Christian Century", there was a certain amount of interest displayed in this science, and an astronomical treatise is among the numerous writings ascribed to the apostate Jesuit Provincial Father Christovão Ferreira, under his Japanese name of Sawano Chuan. The results appear to have been rather meagre, and no radical instance of calendar reform or of astronomical observations can be traced to the influence of the Portuguese in this sphere.

Progress in this branch was further impeded by the fact that the astronomical treatises composed in Chinese by the Jesuits resident at Peking during the XVIIth and XVIIIth centuries, (which could be understood by Japanese classical scholars), were for long banned from Japan in consequence of the celebrated edict prohibiting the import of certain categories of foreign books issued by the Bakufu in 1630. Although contrary to the generally accepted belief the terms of this edict were not framed so as to exclude the importation of all books of Western origin, yet they categorically forbade the importation of any books connected with the Jesuits, whose Sino-European astronomical treatises thus came under

[1] This space is blank in all copies I have examined, but there is a faint mark of some name having been partly impressed, ending in .... *Shiro,* and some words beneath.

the ban. The lack of such works was keenly felt by Japanese scholars and eventually the eighth Tokugawa Shogun, Yoshimune, was persuaded to amend this decree so as to permit the importation of such of these works as had no religious but purely scientific motives [1].

Even prior to this revocation, European astronomical globes and charts had been imported by the Hollanders to Nagasaki, as we learn from the works of the interpreter Nishikawa Joken, who was himself an astronomer of considerable repute. [2] These astronomical works were copied by Japanese artists in Nagasaki, but of original works or of the importation of astronomical books we find little or no trace, so that the importation of the former must be ascribed rather to curiosity than to the zeal for scientific investigation [3]. Probably even if such books had been freely imported it would have been very difficult to secure competent translators, although, as we have mentioned, Nishikawa Joken himself was an astronomer and was summoned by the Shogun to Yedo a few years before his death, in order that his knowledge might be utilised.

Yoshimune seems to have taken an amateur interest in astronomy, and there are several references to his concern for it in the Journals of the *opperhoofden* who were received at court during his tenure of power. He may have acquired this taste (though he was naturally a man of varied interests and great capacity) from the celebrated Arai Hakuseki, who displayed some interest in European astronomy (and other sciences) as a result of his examination of Father Sidotti thereon [4]. Be this as it may, when Yoshimune permitted the importation of the Jesuits' Sino-European astronomical works in 1719, not only was a great advance in this branch of knowledge made possible in Japan, but indirectly another obstacle

[1] See the interesting section devoted to this question (*Yedo Bakufu no Kinsho no naiyo oyobi iwayuru Yosho no ki ni tsuite*) in Professor T. Itazawa's *Rangaku-no-Igi.*

[2] *Shinsen Yogaku Nempyo* in voce Kyoho 4 (1719); p. 1 of the Preface to Vol. I of the *Nagasaki Soshi,* (Nagasaki, 1926). An astronomical work by Nishikawa Joken published in 1720 is listed on p. 118 of Araki's Catalogue, but I have not included it in the bibliography as I think it based on Chinese or Sino-Jesuit rather than on Dutch sources.

[3] Cf. however occasional entries in the *Shinsen Yogaku Nempyo* such as that under Gembun 2 (1737) which records the transcription and translation of two Dutch astronomical charts by the Nagasaki astronomer Kitajima.

[4] Itazawa, *Rangaku no Igi*; Feenstra Kuiper, *Japan en de Buitenwereld,* p. 268.

was put in the way of acquiring this knowledge from Dutch sources; since it was much easier for Japanese scholars to study such works in the classical Chinese which they knew, than in the Dutch language which was only known to a handful of petty officials.

Mainly for this reason, it was not until the penultimate decade of the XVIIIth century that a real advance was made in astronomical knowledge as derived from Dutch sources. The most important factor in this connection was the importation by the Hollanders (apparently in Titsingh's time) of a Dutch edition of J. J. François Lalande's *Astronomie* originally printed at Paris in 1711, (*Astronomia of Sterrekunde vertaald door A. B. Strabbe, bewerkt onder toezicht van C. Douwes,* 1773–1780) [1]. This work came into the hands of the great astronomer, Takahashi Toko, who translated it with the help of several fellow scholars and of his son, the almost equally famous Takahashi Sakuzaemon, who was in later years disgraced on account of his giving Siebold some maps made by Ino Tadataka. The elder Takahashi had studied astronomy under Asada Goritsu (1734–1799) — who himself owed something to Dutch influence — and made use of his knowledge derived from Lalande's work, not only in his official reform of the calendar in 1795, known as the *Kwansei-reki* or calendar of the Kwansei era, but in assisting Ino Tadataka in his great survey of Japan [2]. Keill's astronomical treatise in its Dutch form, *Inleidinge tot de waare Natuur- en sterrekunde of de Natuur en Sterrekundige Lessen* (Leiden, 1741), was the means in translation of familiarising Japanese scholars with the theories of Newton and Napier [3], whilst the calendar reform of the *Tempo* period (1842) owed a great deal to the vastly improved knowledge of the native astronomers as derived from Dutch works.

The works of Takahashi and Shizuki were not common property, as these men were Bakufu officials and their

[1] Itazawa, *Rangaku no Igi*; Feenstra Kuiper, *op. cit.* p. 269. T. Hayashi, *Notes on some astronomical works imported into Japan.* (*Nieuw Archief voor Wiskunde, 2e reeks, VII, etc.* IX;) Idem. *A list of some Dutch astronomical works imported into Japan from Holland.*

[2] *Tadataka Ino,* p. 33. Cf. Krieger, *op. cit.,* p. 105.

[3] Itazawa, *op. cit.* T. Hayashi, *On Shizuki's translation of Keill's astronomical treatise,* in *Nieuw Archief voor Wiskunde,* Deel XI (Amsterdam, 1915).

work was kept more or less secret, being utilised only
for government purposes. Of more 'popular' appeal, though
even then in a somewhat limited sense, were the works
of Shiba Kokan (1737–1818), an interesting personage already briefly alluded to (p. 20), a sketch of whose career
will be found on p. 111 *infra*. Kokan's earlier renown as a
painter has resulted in his being, until very recently at all
events, more famous for his Western-style paintings and
copper-plate engravings which he himself did not think
important, than for his studies in European astronomy,
mathematics and geography. Apparently it was not until he
was fifty that Shiba Kokan took up the study of European
astronomy in 1788, and his first astronomical book was not
printed till eight years later. Professor Muraoka of Sendai
University has published a detailed study of Shiba Kokan
and his astronomical works, both printed and manuscript [1],
which absolves us from the necessity of going into further
detail here. We will conclude this section by giving our usual
list of pioneer works connected with the subject in hand.

1. *Doban Tenkyu Zenzu.* Copper-plate engraving published by Shiba Kokan at Yedo in January, Kwansei 8
   (1796).
2. *Tenmon Chibun Doban Zu.* Twelve coloured copper-
   plate engravings of astronomical, geographical and
   zoological phenomena, with explanatory texts. Published by Shiba Kokan at Yedo in Tenmei 8 (1788).

The plates of astronomical interest are as follows, —

(i) representation of the sun, with sun spots, as seen
through an astronomical telescope; (ii) similar telescopic
view of the moon with its craters etc; (iii) diagram showing
the two rival hypotheses of the earth revolving round the sun,
and of the sun round the earth, with the relative positions of
the earth and moon during spring, summer, autumn and
winter; (iv) action of the moon on the tides; (v) celestial chart
of the heavens in the Northern and Southern hemispheres,
each hemisphere on a separate sheet; (vi) an Orrery, or astronomical instrument named after Charles Boyle, first earl

---

[1] *Tenchi Ridan*, (Tokyo, 1930). Cf. also the article on Shiba Kokan in the *Kokka*,
no. 336, for May 1918, and the more recent one by S. Ayuzawa in *Rekishi-chiri*,
Vol. 72 no: 3, pp. 221–234 (Tokyo, 1938).

PLATE VI   P. 56

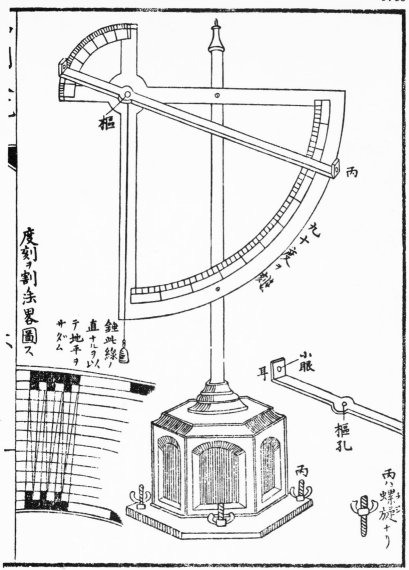

From the original in the author's collection

Illustration from Shiba Kokan's *Oranda Tensetsu* published at Yedo in 1796
(p. 57 of the text)

of Orrery in Ireland (1676–1731). All these plates are hand coloured and have a short explanatory text in Japanese, and the last mentioned is headed in European letters, *Orrery*.

    3 *Oranda Tensetsu* by Shiba Kokan. 1 vol in-4to. published at Yedo in Kwansei 8 (1796).

This volume, which is illustrated with numerous woodcuts derived from European works illustrative of astronomical phenomena, also deals with other matters such as diving bells, which appealed to its author's curious and enquiring mind. This work is now very rare. (See reproduction on Plate VI).

    4 *Kepler Tenmon Zukai* by Shiba Kokan. 2 vols. 4to published at Yedo in Bunkwa 5 (1808).

This treatise, as its name implies, is a translation of an astronomical work by (or based on one of) Kepler, but being guiltless of any knowledge of astronomy I am unable to state the European title of the original work from which it is translated or adapted. Besides several astronomical woodcuts in the text, the work contains an interesting portrait of the translator on p. 3 of the first volume. My own copy of this very rare work is doubly interesting in that it bears the stamp of Hirata Atsutane (1776–1843), the celebrated naturalist and Shinto scholar, whose writings, together with those of Motoori, did so much to undermine the Shogunate and to prepare the way for the Meiji Restoration. In this connection, it is interesting to recall that Hirata Atsutane, despite his uncompromising defence of the Shintoist myths, had a great respect for European scientific knowledge, and in his writings places the Hollanders far above the Chinese in natural science. [1]

---

[1] For further details, cf. the article of Boleslaw Szezsniak, *The penetration of the Copernican Theory into Feudal Japan*, in the *Journal of the Royal Asiatic Society*, April, 1944, pp. 52–61.

IV. THE NAGASAKI INTERPRETERS AND THE STUDY OF DUTCH IN JAPAN

Before we proceed any further, it may be as well to state briefly the linguistic and other abilities of the interpreters at Nagasaki during the period under review, since they formed the main channel of communication between Japan and the outside world as represented by the Hollanders in Deshima.

It is hardly necessary to state that when the Netherlanders first arrived in Japan at the beginning of the XVIIth century, they used not Dutch but Portuguese as their medium of communication with the Japanese. Portuguese was at that time the commercial *lingua franca* of the Far East, and we know from contemporary European sources such as the *Diary* of Richard Cocks, the English factor at Hirado 1613–1623, and the Hirado *Dagh-Registers,* that many Japanese spoke and wrote it with the greatest fluency. In this connection, the praiseworthy linguistic and grammatical works of the Jesuits, many of whom were likewise Japanese scholars of real ability, had exercised considerable influence; but the acquisition of Portuguese was also facilitated by the intermarriage and social intercourse which took place freely between Lusitanians and Japanese prior to 1614. Most Dutch and English East-India ships carried an interpreter or teacher of Portuguese on board, and a knowledge of either the Lusitanian or Castilian tongue was practically a *sine qua non* with any *onder-* or *opper- koopman.* Add to this almost universal knowledge of Portu- guese, the fact that there was nothing to prevent Dutchmen learning Japanese prior to about 1636 [1], and it will be seen

---

[1] Not many Hollanders took the trouble to acquire more than a smattering of collo- quial Japanese, as they found that Portuguese sufficed well enough for the com- mercial transactions they were mainly occupied with during their brief stay in the country. Amongst the exceptions the most notable was François Caron who spent some twenty years in Japan (1619–1641), and acted as interpreter to Pieter Nuyts in 1626–7. Even Caron, though fluent enough in the spoken colloquial language as the Japanese themselves confessed, never mastered the classical written form.

why there were few or no Japanese who could speak Dutch on the occasion of the "closing of the country" and the removal of the Dutch factory from Hirado to Deshima in 1641.

Even after the installation of the Hollanders at Deshima, Portuguese continued to be their principal medium of communication with the Japanese for a considerable number of years. About this time the Japanese interpreters began to study Dutch, but it is clear that their proficiency in this language at first left much to be desired. At the time of the English ship *Return's* visit to Nagasaki in 1673 it was Portuguese rather than Dutch which was the language used, and when the Portuguese ship *São Paulo* came from Macau in 1685, to return some Japanese castaways, there were still a number of interpreters who could read and write Portuguese well [1]. In fact a knowledge of Portuguese was retained by the interpreters down to the end of the XVIIth century at least; but with the waning of Lusitanian commercial and political influence in the Orient, fluency in this language grew less common with the Hollanders, and it became of increasing importance that they should be able to communicate freely in their own tongue with the Japanese.

When the Hollanders first came from Hirado to Deshima in 1641, relations between the personnel of the factory and the Japanese interpreters were anything but satisfactory. Most of the latter had been closely connected with the Portuguese for whom they still retained a sneaking if closely concealed sympathy, and disputes with the newcomers were of almost daily occurrence. The Journals and reports of the *opperhoofden* at Deshima during the XVIIth century are filled with bitter complaints of the inefficiency, dishonesty, rapacity and corruption of the Japanese interpreters, and though these strictures are no doubt greatly exaggerated, readers of Valentyn and Kaempfer will probably agree that they were deserved to some extent [2].

Before long, affairs were so bad that both sides made some efforts to improve the situation. In 1673, perhaps as a conse-

---

[1] Cf. the documents about this mission printed in the *Arquivos de Macau*. Vol. I, pp. 219–234.

[2] Cf. Boxer, *Jan Compagnie in Japan.* p. 148 (*Trans. As. Soc. Japan*, II Series, Vol. VII. 1931).

quence of the *Return*'s visit, the Governor of Nagasaki
decided to send some youths to study Dutch under the Hollanders at Deshima with a view to their becoming efficient
interpreters, as is recorded in the *opperhoofd*'s *Dagh-Register*
under 9th November — "The interpreters come to inform
us that the Governor has decided and ordered that a certain
Japanese boy, about ten or twelve years old, will come here
daily on the island, in order to learn Dutch from one of
the Company's servants, as likewise to be taught how to
read and write the same" [1]). There are other references to
apprentice students of Dutch and Portuguese in 1684–5,
and subsequent years. However, the Hollanders were not
statisfied with these measures, and in 1675, Governor-General Maetsuycker wrote to the Governor of Nagasaki com-
plaining of the inefficiency of the interpreters and requesting
that the Hollanders might be allowed to learn Japanese,
but this last request was rejected [2].

Matters thus continued for some time on their former
footing, though there seems to have been a slight easing of
the tension towards the end of the century. The personnel at
Deshima appear to have grown gradually more complacent in
their attitude, either because of their own increasing lethargy,
or else in consequence of a growing ability amongst the interpreters. It may be mentioned in passing that communications
from the Governor-General at Batavia to the Nagasaki officials or Shogunal authorities were frequently sent in Chinese.
There were plenty of Chinese at Batavia who were capable
of drawing up official documents or petitions, and even a few
Dutchmen who had some knowledge of the language; and
it seems to have been felt that there was more chance of a
letter in classical Chinese reaching and being understood by
the intended recipient, than in a Dutch missive which the
interpreters were free to falsify or mistranslate if it suited
them to do so.

The interpreters at Nagasaki were formed into a sort of
guild or college and divided into *Dai-Tsuji*, senior interpreters,

---

[1] Quoted on p. 465 of Professor T. Itazawa's *Tsujika no Oranda Gogaku* (Pt. III of
his *Rangaku no Igi*) whence much of the material for this present section has been
derived.
[2] Reproduced in translation by Boxer, in *Trans. As. Soc. Japan*, loc. cit. pp. 199–200.

and *Ko-Tsuji* or junior interpreters, besides apprentice or student-interpreters (leerling-Tolken). Their occupation seems to have been largely an hereditary one, as the same names keep on recurring from the middle of the XVIIth century down to the end of the Tokugawa period. Amongst the most famous of the hereditary interpreter families, we may mention those of Motoki (or Motogi), Narabayashi, Nishi and Kobayashi. Some of these families were descended from the original interpreters to the Portuguese, whilst others were of Hirado origin, having come thence with the Hollanders on their removal to Deshima in 1641. Their rates of pay seem to have varied considerably from time to time, but we learn from the *Dagh-Register* of 1675 that *Dai-Tsuji* were then paid at the rate of 1,000 silver taels p.a. and *Ko-Tsuji* at 400 taels [1].

It is often stated in books on Japanese history, both native and foreign, that the study of Dutch by the Nagasaki interpreters was originally limited by law to oral instruction and that they were first allowed to read Dutch books by an order of Yoshimune in 1720. This belief though widely held is quite erroneous, and it is clear from contemporary records that there was never any ban on Japanese interpreters learning to read and write Dutch. As early as 1644, we read in the *opperhoofd*'s journal that a statement of his was taken down in Dutch by the interpreters ("the foregoing was taken down by the interpreters in writing in Portuguese, Dutch, and Japanese.... we being made to sign the same"), although as we have seen, their knowledge of both the written and spoken word for long left much to be desired [2].

Two things have contributed to the commonly accepted but erroneous belief that it was not until the time of Yoshimune that the interpreters received official permission to study Dutch books. The first is the idea that the ban on the importation of books connected with Christianity in 1630

---

[1] Itazawa. *Rangaku no Igi*. p. 465.

[2] *Ibid.* p. 461. According to Professor Itazawa (*Rangaku no Igi*, p. 589) this alleged decree by Yoshimune revoking the ban on the import of Dutch books, was taught from the historical text-books prescribed for use in the Government Middle Schools in Japan in 1936. Under these circumstances it seems doubtful if this fable will ever be eradicated, especially as most standard Western histories of Japan contain it also.

likewise included all European books, which Professor Itazawa has conclusively proved not to have been the case. In actual fact the Bakufu never issued a general prohibition of European books, nor was this necessary in view of the ignorance of European languages which was almost universal in Japan between 1640 and 1860. By the decree of 1630, and other similar ones published subsequently, only works connected with Christianity or scientific treatises composed by the Jesuits in China were prohibited from being imported; and it was the ban on certain of these works which was raised by Yoshimune in 1719 and not a (non-existent) ban on Dutch books [1]. Another contributory cause of misunderstanding is the statement in some Japanese histories that certain interpreters were first expressly commanded to study Dutch books at dates variously given as 1719, 1745 and *c*. 1750. This statement (which seems to have originated in Otsuki Gentaku's *Rangaku koto hajime*) evidently refers to Yoshimune ordering the interpreters to study some special Dutch books for a specific purpose, and not to a general permission to study a hitherto prohibited subject.

This belief, mistaken though it be, contains an element of truth in that it was from the time of Yoshimune that the Nagasaki interpreters began to acquire a real proficiency in Dutch, whether oral or written. From this time also dates the origin of the *Rangakusha* or amateur Dutch scholars, who strove to acquire their knowledge of the language by their own efforts and independently of the official interpreters. The struggles and achievements of these scholars such as Aoki Bunzo (Konyo), Otsuki Gentaku, Sugita Gempaku and others are fairly well known to all students of Japanese history so we need not deal with them here [2]. But

[1] See Professor Itazawa's *Yedo Bakufu no Kinsho no Naiyo oyobi iwayuru Yosho no kin ni suite*, on pp. 568–591 of his *Rangaku no Igi* wherein a list of the books actually prohibited will be found. Cf. also S. Sakanishi, *Prohibition of certain Chinese books and the policy of the Yedo government*, in *Journal of the American Oriental Society*, Vol. 57, pp. 290–303 (September, 1937) and Père Henri Bernard-Maître S. J., *Traductions chinoises d'ouvrages européens au Japon durant la période de fermeture, 1614– 1853*, in *Monumenta Nipponica*, III, pp. 40–60, (Tokyo, 1940).

[2] The best general accounts are Professor Murdoch, *History of Japan*, Vol. III, Ch. XV, pp. 537–568. Dr. Feenstra Kuiper, *Japan en de Buitenwereld*, pp. 225–259. Cf. also Mitsukuri, *The Early Study of Dutch in Japan*(*Trans. As. Soc. Japan* Vol. V.) *Tadataka Ino*, passim, and various articles in *Trans. As. Soc. Japan*. For Aoki Bunzo's works on

it may be as well to point out, as Professor Murdoch and Dr. Feenstra Kuiper have already suggested, that the achievements of the *Rangakusha*, meritorious as they indubitably were, have been considerably exaggerated at the expense of the Nagasaki interpreters, who are usually represented as wilfully obstructing the progress of the former.

It is true that there was a certain amount of jealousy between them, and in the beginning at all events, the interpreters created unnecessary difficulties. But relations between the two groups undoubtedly improved towards the close of the XVIIIth century; and some interpreters like Motogi were of real value and assistance to Otsuki Gentaku, Shiba Kokan and other *Rangakusha*. It must be remembered that the interpreters, as government officials, were not at liberty to impart their specialised knowledge to all and sundry who wished to share it; but when they received official permission or encouragement to do so they were extremely helpful [1].

The aspersions that have been cast on their linguistic capacities are quite unjustified in so far as the last quarter of the XVIIIth century is concerned, and both Thunberg and Titsingh bear witness to their qualifications. The words of the latter are particularly interesting in this connection. "Far from finding them" (he writes) "suspicious and reluctant, as Europeans are usually pleased to represent these persons in order to palliate their own indolence, they manifested, on the contrary, an eagerness to procure for me every practicable information, to consult in various matters beyond their capacity the best informed individuals among the magistrates and clergy, and to furnish me with books which might serve as a guide to my labours." That this testimony was no exaggeration is easily proved by the correspondence between Titsingh and his Japanese friends, some of whose original letters, written in fluent Dutch, are preserved in the library of the Imperial University of Kyoto. These are referred to again in the section on Isaac Titsingh (p. 148 *infra*), and it is only necessa-

the Dutch language (which remained Mss.) cf. *Shinsen Yogaku Nempyo* and Araki's Catalogue (p. 1). Cf. Krieger, *op. cit.*, pp. 28, 30–56.

[1] Examinations of the interpreters in Dutch are recorded as being held by the *opperhoofd* on the orders of the Bugyo of Nagasaki in 1768 and 1778. There are probably other instances. Fully qualified interpreters were apparently tested orally and in writing. (Iatazawa, *Rangaku no Igi.* p. 468).

ry to observe here that this mastery of the Dutch language by
Nagasaki interpreters did not cease with the departure of
Titsingh, but continued to maintain the same high level of
excellence for many years. Especially during the Napoleonic
period and the time of the *opperhoofd* Hendrik Doeff (1803–
1817), did their abilities find greater scope in the compilation
of various Dutch-Japanese vocabularies, dictionaries and
grammatical treatises, some of the earliest of which are listed
below. In conclusion it is worth noting that although the
study of Russian, French and English was begun by the Japanese about this time, Dutch continued to be the official
language for the transaction of foreign affairs down to the
third year of Meiji (1870), and it was not until two years later
that the governmental Dutch language schools were closed
and replaced by institutions where English, French and
German were taught instead.

     1. *Rangaku Kaitei* by Otsuki Gentaku. 2 vols in-4to.
       Printed at Yedo in Tenmei 8 (1788).

This is the first work ever composed and printed by Japanese which deals exclusively with the study of a European
language, as the Japanese-Portuguese dictionaries and gram-
mars published during the early years of the XVIIth century
were the works of European Jesuits. The author, Otsuki Gentaku, (also commonly called Bansui) was a native of Sendai in
N.E. Japan and the founder of a long line of *Rangakusha*. He
first studied Dutch under Sugita Gempaku (principal author
of the *Kaitai Shinsho*, cf. p. 47 *supra*) and Maeno Rankwa
(Ryotaku), subsequently going to Nagasaki where he stayed
for a considerable time in the house of the Motogi family of
interpreters in order to perfect his knowledge. The present
work was published after his return from Nagasaki to Yedo,
and its appearance gave a great impetus to the study of Dutch.
The first volume deals with the method of studying Dutch,
and contains various commendatory prefaces which occupy
nearly half of the book. The second volume contains the
essence of the work, such as the Roman alphabet, lists of
Roman and Arabic numerals, the *iroha* kana syllabry arranged in Roman letters, various groups of vowels and consonants,
method of pronounciation, and a few simple examples illustrating the construction of sentences such as *Ik wensch U*

PLATE VII
P. 64

メン レ｜レン
men leeren.
人　習

老タルヲハン
敬フベシ少ガ
ヲハ習フス
ベシ
ヘイ　フ　レングト
Hy brengt gant-
他　終
ナグテン　メット
sche nagten met
夜　以
レ｜セン　ドｰル
leesen door.
書　讀　徹

イキ　望ンス　ユ　グｰ
Jk wensch u goe
我　望　你　吉

デン　ダク　メイン　ヘール
den dag myn heer.
日　君　吾

我貴君ノ
嘉日ヲ希
望ス
イキ　ベン　ユ　ディ・ナｰル
Jk ben u dienaar.
我　者　你　臣

オッデン　ザル　メン
Ouden zal men
老　可　人

イキ　ヘッブ　アル　ノイン
Jk heb al myn
我　悉　吾

エ｜レン　ヨンゲン　サル
eeren jongen zal
敬　少　可

A page of Otsuki Gentaku's *Rangaku Kaitei (First steps in Dutch)* published at Yedo in 1788

goeden dag mijn heer; Ouden zal men eeren, jongen zal men leeren; wit raven vind men zelden alzo zelden men trouwen; and *Een onsterfelijken naam, onsterflijken roem verkrijgen.* Nevertheless, although a praiseworthy pioneer effort, the book leaves a great deal to be desired from even the most elementary student's point of view, not the least of its faults being the almost total lack of a vocabulary, which is limited to two pages containing some thirty-two simple words such as heaven, earth, red, yellow, autumn, winter, man, woman, &c.

Although the date of publication is given at the end as being Tenmei 8 (1788), the prefaces and epilogue are dated Tenmei 3 (1783). A typical page is reproduced in Plate VII.

    2. *Zoko Rangaku Hai* by Yoshikawa. I sheet (album). printed in Kwansei 7 (1795).

The author was a pupil of Otsuki Gentaku. There was a reprint in 1810.

    3. *Bango Sen* by Katsuragawa Hoshu. 1 vol. published in Kwansei 10 (1798).

A good description of this work is given on pp. 256-7 of Dr. Feenstra Kuiper's *Japan en de Buitenwereld in de XVIIIe eeuw* which obviates the necessity of describing it here.

    4. *Haruma Wakai* (On cover) *F. Halma, Nederduits Woordenboek;* by Inamura Sampaku. Kwansei 8(1796). 32(?) vols.

The author of this work was a physician of the Ikeda (Tottori) clan who was inspired to learn Dutch by a perusal of Otsuki Gentaku's *Rangaku Kaitei.* He became a disciple of Gentaku and also spent some time studying the language at Nagasaki, but soon became convinced of the necessity for an extensive Dutch-Japanese vocabulary. He therefore determined to translate François Halma's Dutch-French dictionary into Japanese, translating for this purpose over 80,000 words. He was only able to print 30 parts which he distributed (or sold?) amongst his fellow *Rangakusha.* No complete set of this work remains or was ever printed, and only a very few odd parts have survived to this day. One of these (letters U, V), in the possession of Professor Katsumata of Waseda University, I was able to examine by the courtesy of the owner when in Japan. The Dutch words are printed in movable type wood-blocks. Inamura's work is known as the *Yedo*

Halma, and must be distinguished from a subsequent con-
tinuation printed at Kyoto, and from the manuscript *Halma*
dictionary compiled by ten of the Deshima interpreters under the supervision of Hendrik Doeff. Probably the *Doeff
Halma* was based upon the *Yedo Halma* or some manuscript
copy thereof, of which there are several still extant.

     5. *Rango Yakusen.* By Okudaira Shoko. 6 vols. printed
        at Kyoto in Bunkwa 7 (1810). Apparently a short
        Dutch-Japanese vocabulary of astronomical and zo-
        ological terms.

The author was a retainer of the Daimyo of Nakatsu in
Buzen (Kyushu).

     6. *Yakken.* By Fujibayashi Fusan. 2 vols. and 1 vol.
        addenda published in Bunkwa 7 (1810).

This work is an abridged version of Inamura's great *Yedo
Halma.* The supplementary volume was reissued later in another form under the title of *Yakken Hanrei*; it is not part of
the vocabulary, but rather a grammatical treatise on the lines
of the *Rangaku Kaitei* of 1788, but more detailed. Professors
Katsumata and Itazawa state that 100 copies of this work were
printed in movable types. Such copies are now excessively
rare, and even the ordinary wood-block edition is hard to
procure. Fujibayashi Fusan was the author of several grammatical and medical works translated or adapted from the
Dutch, including the following.

     7. *Oranda Gohokai.* 3 vols in-4to. Published at Osaka in
        Bunkwa 9 (1812).

We have not space to record the numerous works dealing
with the study of the Dutch language published during the
first quarter of the XIXth century, but the following is worth
recording as the prototype of numerous subsequent works.

     8. *Oranda Bunten.* 1 vol. published at Yedo in Bunsei 11
        (1828).

This book is a textual reproduction of the *Grammatica ofte
Nederduitsche Spraakkunst. Uitgegeven door de Maatschappÿ
tot nut van 't algemeen. Tweede druk. Leyden, Deventer en Groningen &c.* 1822. Title-page, preface and text are all copied
from the Dutch original and printed from wood-blocks in
imitation of a fine cursive hand. This is the very rare *editio
princeps,* the editions usually met with being the subsequent
reprints of 1840–1842.

V. PICTORIAL ARTS

I. *Nagasaki-e*

a) *General*. Nagasaki-e may be defined as colour-prints made from wood-blocks and published in Nagasaki. They form a branch of the popular art of Old Japan which has been unduly neglected by connoisseurs of Japanese Art until very recent years. Even in the land of their origin they attracted no attention, whilst not one of the numerous and voluminous books on Japanese colour-prints published by eminent native and foreign authorities before 1924 devoted as much as a few lines to them. Their very existence was ignored or forgotten, and even the rarest specimens might have been picked up for a few yen apiece.

Within the last twenty years, however, a complete change has taken place in this respect. Following on Professor G. Kuroda's masterly essay in his *Seiyo no Eikyo wo uketaru Nihongwa* (Kyoto, 1924), which is still the standard work on the subject, some interest began to be taken in these prints by art collectors in Japan. The works of Mr. Nagami [1], himself an enthusiastic collector of Nagasaki-e, provided a further stimulus to their popularity, and consequently to their prices, which now, in the case of the older examples, bid fair to rival the sums demanded for the better known works of the Ukiyoe artists. The present writer during his stay in Japan was fortunate enough to start collecting these prints when their popularity had as yet scarcely begun, and he was enabled to examine several hundred examples in the possession of the leading art dealers, as well as in the principal private collections. Amongst the former may be specially mentioned Shimidzu Gensendo of Tokyo, [2] Misumi of Osaka

---

[1] Principally the *Nagasaki Hangwa Shu*, and the *Zoku Nagasaki Hangwa Shu*, (Tokyo, Taisho 15 or 1926).

[2] The regrettable fact that this worthy dealer was imprisoned for faking works of

and Hosokawa in Kyoto; whilst the late Netherlands Minister in Tokyo, General J. C. Pabst, and Mr. Ikenaga of Kobe, who owned the two richest and most representative collections of Nagasaki-e in 1936, were kind enough to allow the writer to study them at leisure. To the former he is further indebted for his enthusiastic coöperation and advice, alike in this as in so many other matters relating to the history of his countrymen in Japan. Finally, the writer has had the advantage of having been able to discuss Nagasaki-e with such eminent connoisseurs and investigators as Professor G. Kuroda, Mr. T. Nagami, Professor I. Shimmura, Dr. J. Koga and the late Dr. T. Nagayama of Nagasaki. It is owing to the fortunate circumstance of having been enabled to confer with such leading authorities that he feels emboldened to introduce these prints to the notice of European readers, although painfully conscious of his lack of that critical or artistic ability which is so desirable when dealing with a subject like the present [1].

b) *Characteristics of Nagasaki-e.* It is essential, and fortunately not very difficult, to distinguish Nagasaki-e from colour-prints published at Yedo, Kyoto and Osaka during the XVIIIth and first half of the XIXth centuries. The chief difference lies in the subject *motif.* Nagasaki-e may be regarded as a branch of the Ukiyoe or "floating world" prints in a certain sense, but the world they portray is an entirely different one from that so ably depicted by the Yedo masters. As is well-known, the Ukiyoe prints deal with such subjects as the fair but frail beauties of the so-called gay quarters; with warriors, wrestlers, actors and theatrical subjects in

---

art on a large scale in 1934–5, does not reflect on his undoubted ability as a connoisseur of *Nagasaki-e*; and the present writer at all events will long retain a grateful remembrance of this genial personage and of his tireless efforts to secure colour-prints from all quarters.

[1] The best works available for the study of Nagasaki prints are by Professor G. Kuroda, *Seiyo no eikyo wo uketaru Nihongwa* (Kyoto, 1924); T. Nagami, *Nagasaki Hangwa-shu* and *Zoku Nagasaki Hangwa-shu,* (Tokyo, 1926); T. Ikenaga, *Hosaibankwa Daihokan,* (2 vols., Osaka, 1933); N. H. Mody, *A collection of Nagasaki colourprints and paintings showing the influence of Chinese and European art on that of Japan,* (2 vols., London & Kobe, 1939). General J. C. Pabst generously bequeathed his collection to the present writer in 1941, but I do not know what has become of Mr. Mody's since since his death during the Pacific War. Mr. Ikenaga's collection is now housed in a Museum at Kobe.

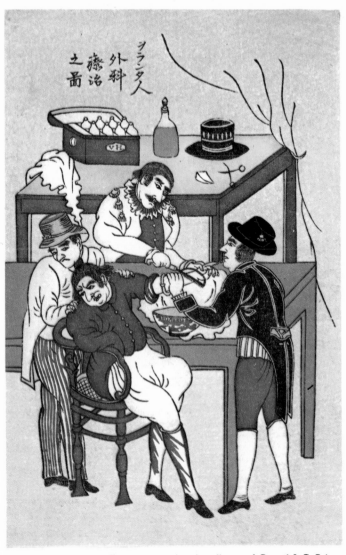

From the original in the collection of General J. C. Pabst

A typical Nagasaki colour-print, *circa* 1815

general; with birds, flowers, scenery, and, not infrequently, with the most licentious or suggestive scenes. Nagasaki-e on the other hand, as their name implies, deal only with subjects connected with the port of Nagasaki in general, and with the Hollanders or Chinese who frequented it in particular. In other words, the "floating world" which they portray is that centered round the Dutch and Chinese factories in Nagasaki and bounded by the steep hills which border the narrow fjord-like entrance to its bay. Typical subjects of these prints are the Dutch and Chinese shipping which frequented the harbour; Hollanders and Chinamen, either singly or in pairs; exotic animals or birds such as elephants, camels, cassuaries and parrots imported by the foreigners; views of the Dutch and Chinese factories, and so forth. If the prints deal with scenery, then it is always some aspect of Nagasaki bay with Dutch or Chinese shipping in the offing; if they deal, as is only rarely the case, with frail beauties or merry parties, then it is not the gaily bedizend prostitute who is the centre of attraction as in the Yedo Ukiyoe, but her Dutch or Chinese patrons. It is worth noting also — again in strong contrast to the Yedo and Kyoto style prints — that no obscene or even suggestive theme is ever portrayed, unless the above-mentioned examples of prostitutes and foreigners are regarded as such. It is perhaps unnecessary to add that although these prints deal with many aspects of things foreign, a religious *motif* is never discernible, in consequence of the rigorous ban against anything connected with Christianity maintained by the Bakufu from 1641 till its fall over two hundred years later [1].

Amongst other characteristics of Nagasaki-e, the following are worth a passing mention. Very few of these prints are signed by the artist; and of these few, the majority are late examples dating from about 1840–1850. Foreign influence is perceptible not only in the design, but also to some extent in the materials used. This is especially the case with the earlier prints, some of which are clearly derived from Dutch copper-plate engravings or copied from Chinese originals of the late

[1] It is perhaps unnecessary to point out that these Nagasaki colour-prints have no connection with the woodcuts and engravings published by the Jesuit missionaries and their converts at Nagasaki, and neighbouring places c. 1592–1610. These had long been destroyed or forgotten, and exercised no influence on the origin and growth of Nagasaki-e.

Ming dynasty. Sometimes European pigments were used for the colours applied by hand, and Chinese paper was quite often employed. The colours principally used in the early prints of *c.* 1760–1790 were *cha-iro* (*lit.* tea-colour) or light brown, indigo, red and black. In the beginning of the XIXth century Nagasaki-e begin to develop a tendency to approximate more closely to Yedo-e or ordinary Ukiyoe in technique and colouring, although they can always be readily distinguished, as the former retain their predominantly foreign and exotic themes. This tendency grows more noticeable as the years go by, and finally Nagasaki-e become practically indistinguishable from the so-called Yokohama-e after 1860 [1]. Nagasaki-e vary greatly in size (and also in shape), but generally speaking the oldest ones are the largest; some of them measuring more than 60 × 80 centimeters. Another point worth noting is that they frequently have a long and detailed description or explanation of the subject portrayed, which is seldom if ever the case with ordinary Ukiyoe prints.

We have already mentioned that the artists rarely signed their works, although the name of the publishing firm is usually, but by no means invariably, to be found affixed to the print in some form or other. Little or nothing therefore is known of the actual artists, but it seems probable, as Mr. Nagami Tokutaro has suggested, that they were persons connected in some way (probably officially) with either the Dutch or Chinese factories. The ordinary inhabitant of Nagasaki had little opportunity for more than brief glimpses of the foreigners; and as many of these prints were clearly drawn from life, it seems reasonable to suppose that they were designed in the first place by men who had some opportunity to view the foreign barbarians more closely than most of their fellows. Perhaps some of the poorer, but more artistically-inclined interpreters or pretty officials, earned an honest penny in their spare time by originating such designs. In any case it is clear they were executed by people in humble circumstances, as they were mostly printed on paper of poor

---

[1] These Yokohama-e were really printed at Yedo, but as they dealt with the life of the new seaport and particularly with its foreign community they came to be known as Yokohama-e, and soon supplanted the Nagasaki-e entirely.

quality and sold very cheaply [1]. They were intended for sale to tourists, merchants, scholars, and to all who came from other parts of Japan to visit Nagasaki, whether for business or pleasure, and who wished to take back with them to their native provinces some tangible evidence of the curious sights they had seen in the exotic atmosphere of the port with its Red-haired Barbarian and Chinese visitors.

c) *Chronology of Nagasaki-e.* The origin of Nagasaki-e is uncertain. According to the most generally accepted views amongst Japanese scholars and collectors, the oldest known Nagasaki-e is the world map, with its accompanying woodcut of 42 types of foreigners, which is supposed to have been printed at Nagasaki in the cyclical cock-year of Shoho, or at some date between 1644 and 1648. This map and its authenticity have already been discussed in some detail in the cartographical section of this essay (cf. p. 9) and the map itself need not be described again here. The present writer is inclined to accept the arguments advanced by Mr. Ikenaga in his *Hosaibankwa Daihokan* against the ascription of this map to Nagasaki, and to agree with the Japanese connoisseur that it is more likely to be an Osaka or Kyoto piece of work, on which the publisher put the name of Nagasaki in order to avoid compromising himself with the Bakufu officials, who were then intensely suspicious of anything pertaining to foreign intercourse. On the other hand, some indirect support can be cited for believing it to have been in reality a Nagasaki work. The principal point in support of this thesis, is the statement made by Nishikawa Joken in his *Nagasaki Yawagusa,* that world maps and astronomical charts were amongst the things made at Nagasaki after Western models in the second half of the XVIIth century. But he does not specifically mention colour-prints in this or indeed in any other connection, and the probality is that these maps were only manuscript copies or tracings of European originals.

---

[1] According to the *Nagasaki Miyage* published in 1847, small prints were then sold for 24 *mon* (one *mon* was the equivalent of a farthing or cent) and large ones of the Nagasaki map size for 96 *mon*. The cost of living in Nagasaki as one of the five Shogunal towns (the others were Yedo, Kyoto, Osaka and Sakai) was rather higher than elsewhere in Japan, and 96 *mon* were equivalent to about 100 in most places. But even so the price did not amount to more than a few pence.

The most powerful argument against this Shoho map being a Nagasaki work, is the inexplicable length of time which elapsed before another dated colour-print was made in Nagasaki, namely more than one hundred years. This print is the map of the town and harbour of Nagasaki made by Ohata Bunjiyemon, the founder of the famous Toshimaya publishing firm which produced many of the most attractive and artistic colour-prints published in Nagasaki during the next fifty years. The map is dated Horeki 14 or 1764, and even though some of the undated colour-prints produced by the Hariya firm are undoubtedly older than this, yet the oldest of these cannot date from before about 1720, so that even then there remains a gap of nearly one hundred years between the Shoho world map and the next oldest Nagasaki-e. It is of course possible that the Shoho map was merely an isolated phenomenon, but this seems unlikely; and although the question cannot be definitely decided one way or the other until further evidence is produced, it seems best to accept its classification as a Nagasaki production *cum grano salis*. In another sense it is markedly different from all other known Nagasaki-e, and world maps as a subject do not recur until the middle years of the nineteenth century, so that on this ground too, its ascription to Nagasaki seems doubtful. Whether the original was taken from some Western or from a Sino-European model is also uncertain. Professor Kuroda inclines to the latter view, and believes both sections of it to be closely copied from some Chinese original of the late Ming period. The map measures 3 *shaku* 6 *sun* by 1 *shaku* $5^1/_5$ *sun* [1]. It is printed on six sheets joined together and hand-coloured in five tints, yellow, orange, violet, green, and grey.

The next oldest known Nagasaki-e, or, if we reject the classification of the Shoho map as Nagasaki-e, the oldest of all Nagasaki-e, are the works published by a firm called Hariya and which date from about 1750 or earlier. Only three types of these Hariya prints are known, and the only existing set of these three is in the collection of Mr. Ikenaga of Kobe who paid a very high price for them, running into several thous-

---

[1] 1 *shaku* = 30.3 cm. and 1 *sun* = 3.03 cm.

ands of yen if I am not mistaken [1]. None of these three prints are dated, but there can be no doubt that they are older than the Horeki 14 map of Nagasaki for reasons which are adduced further on.

Continuing in chronological sequence, the next oldest Nagasaki-e in point of time, are those published by the firm of Toshimaya already mentioned. To this firm belongs the distinction of having produced the first dated Nagasaki-e, in the Horeki 14 (1764) map which served as the prototype for all subsequent maps of Nagasaki for the next hundred years. It must however be noticed in passing that this was not the earliest printed map of Nagasaki, but only the first map of the city actually printed there. Amongst the earlier woodcuts of Nagasaki may be cited those of Empo (c. 1673), probably oldest of all in point of time, Hoei 8 (1705), and Enkyo 2 (1745) of which the first was published at Yedo in all probability and the other two at Kyoto. Furthermore there is a large undated map of Nagasaki published by a certain Nakamura Sanzo of Chikujuken in Nagasaki, of which there are at least two known variants and which several competent authorities believe to be considerably older than Toshimaya's Horeki 14 print.

Reverting to the prints published by the firm of Toshimaya founded by Ohata Bunjiyemon, the following is a list of the most important of them, arranged as far as possible in chronological order. Some of them are unsigned, but can be classified as being the work of Toshimaya with reasonable certainty. This list does not pretend to include any save the most important ones, since the firm lasted until the Bunsei period and had published scores of prints by that time.

Date	Title or legend on print	Stamp, seal, or signature
1. Horeki 14, 8th month (1764)	Map of Nagasaki in Hishu (= Hizen).	Ohata Bunjiyemon. of Katsuyama street Nagasaki.
2. Annei 7, 8th month (1778).	,,	,,

[1] These prints are reproduced on a large scale (one of them in colour) on Plates 152–4 of his *Hosaibankwa Daihokan*. Professor Kuroda has smaller reproductions in monochrome in his work.

Date	Title or legend on print	Stamp, seal, or signature
3. Annei 9, (1780).	View of Hollanders' factory in Deshima.	Toshimaya Bunjiyemon of Katsuyama street Nagasaki.
4. Annei 9, (1780).	View of Chinese factory	,,
5. Tenmei 2 (1782).	Picture of Hollander ship	Toshima Denkichi of Nagasaki.
6. Tenmei 3 (1783).	Pictorial map of Kyushu.	Toshimaya.
7. Kwansei 2 (1790).	Pictorial explanation of Hollander ship.	Unsigned.
8. Kwansei 8 (1796).	Map of Nagasaki in Hishu.	Toshimaya of Katsuyama street.
9. Bunkwa 8 (1812).	Picture of Chosen Embassy's Procession.	Toshimaya.
10. Bunkwa 14 (1817).	Hollander woman.	Unsigned.
11. Bunsei 4 (1821).	Map of Nagasaki in Hishu.	The original woodblock artist of Katsuyama street, Toshimaya.

Not long after the foundation of the Toshimaya by Ohata Bunjiyemon during the Horeki era (1751–1764), was established the rival firm of Bunkindo, which eventually supplanted the older house. The oldest dated print bearing the Bunkindo impress is the map of Nagasaki published in Kyowa 2 (1802) to which more detailed allusion will be made later, but there is no doubt that the firm started production about the Tenmei-Kwansei periods c. 1780–1790. There is considerable difficulty in distinguishing some of the earlier productions of the Bunkindo from those of Toshimaya, as also its later works from those of other publishing houses which flourished contemporaneously with it during the XIXth century. The latest dated example of a Bunkindo print is Kaei 4 (1851) but it is certain that the firm continued to publish unsigned prints for some years longer. By way of illustrating the difficulty of disentangling the priority of the various prints published at Nagasaki during the early XIXth century, we may instance the five maps of Nagasaki published by four different publishers in the same year of Kyowa 1 (1801) [1].

The third great publishing-house of Nagasaki-e, the Yamatoya was established much later than its predecessors, at

[1] See p. 59 of Prof. Kuroda's *Seiyo no Eikyo wo uketaru Nihongwa* for further details, and the prints and maps reproduced in Vol. I of the Mody Catalogue.

about the end of the Tempo period or *c.* 1840. Both this house
as several minor firms which existed about this time, flourished exceedingly during the Tempo, Ansei and Kaei periods
(*c.* 1830–1860), and consequently prints of this age are relatively common. In contrast to the productions of the Yamatoya and Bunkindo firms the prints of Toshimaya are rare,
those before 1800 exceedingly so, whilst the earliest efforts of
Hariya are, as we have seen, practically unprocurable at the
present day.

d) *Descriptive classification of Nagasaki-e.* — (i) *Hariya.*
The colour-prints published by Hariya about the middle of
the XVIIIth century, may well be termed the oldest Nagasaki-e in the strictest sense of the term .For even if the Shoho
print was really a Nagasaki work, we have seen that its origin
and design have nothing in common with any other Nagasaki
colour prints, and that it is only a copy of some foreign
design allegedly executed at the Kyushu port. The subjects
of the Hariya prints on the other hand, were repeated in
countless subsequent productions of the Toshimaya, Bunkindo, Yamatoya and other schools. They are not merely
isolated copies of some foreign original, as is the Shoho map,
but recognizably drawn from life, and are full of that local
colour which is the true charm of the genuine Nagasaki-e.

From their appearance, design and technique, Professor
Kuroda deduced the fact that, although undated, they must
be older than the map of Nagasaki by Toshimaya published
in 1764. He places these Hariya prints at about 1750, or a little
earlier, and if one may judge from the costume of the Hollander depicted in one of them, they may well date from about
1730, if the original sketch was drawn from life as was probably
the case [1].

Another argument in favour of the priority of these Hariya
prints in point of age is their excessive rarity. Only three
types of prints are known, namely those depicting a Hollan-

[1] Cf. reproduction of this plate on Pl. 152 of Vol. II of Ikenaga's Catalogue. Incidentally the print is an interesting contribution to the iconography of the Hollanders
in Asia during this period. The *opperhoofd's* coat bears distinct traces of Asiatic
influence in the design and was probably made by some native or Chinese tailor. Note
also the wine (? or brandy) bottle and glass, with the long clay pipe, both frequently
recurring subjects in many subsequent Nagasaki-e, as also in the representations of
Hollanders in the glyptic and applied arts (netsuke, tsuba, inro, &c).

der, a Chinaman, and a Chinese ship. Of these the first is unique, whilst of the other two types only two examples of each have so far been traced. As already mentioned, Mr. Ikenaga of Kobe is the fortunate possessor of the only known complete set of three. Judging from subsequent similar sets published by other firms it seems probable that another print representing a Dutch ship was originally published to complete the set to four prints, but, if so, no copy of this has hitherto been traced. The three existing prints are lettered as follows, —

1. *Oranda-jin no Zu. Nagasaki Sakura-machi Hariya. Picture of a Hollander.* [Published by] *Hariya of Sakura street, Nagasaki.* With additional explanation in *kana* of the Hollander and his Javanese (Jap. "kurombo" lit. "black") slave.
2. No title, but *Shin Cho-jin no Zu* understood. *Nagasaki Sakura-machi Hariya. Picture of a Chinaman of the Shin* (= *Tsing or Manchu*) *Dynasty. Hariya of Sakura street, Nagasaki.*
3. *To sen no Zu. Nagasaki Sakura-machi. Picture of Chinese ship. Hariya of Sakura street, Nagasaki.* With thirteen lines of explanatory text giving dimensions of the ship and table of distances from Japan to various places in China. In contrast to the other two prints, this one is oblong.

All these three prints are hand-coloured, the tints chiefly employed being light blue, brown, dull red and a very pale yellow.

ii) *Toshimaya* or *Toyoshimaya* [1]. This was the trade-name adopted by Ohata Bunjiyemon, the founder of this firm. Although Bunjiyemon may have published some prints before 1764, the oldest work of his which can be dated with certainty is the map of Nagasaki published by him in that year, and already alluded to more than once. As the oldest dated map actually printed in that city itself, space may be found here for a rather more detailed description of it.

---

[1] The first character is usually pronounced *Toyo*, but both Professor Kuroda and Mr. Nagami are agreed that the reading in this case should be *Toshimaya* and not *Toyoshimaya*. The name was also sometimes written with another initial character, namely the Fu (*tomi*, *to*[-*mu*]) of Mount Fuji, but here used for the sound of its second alternative reading of *to*.

The map measures about 100 by 65 centimetres along its outer borders as measured by my own copy. The square in the bottom left-hand corner contains the title *Hishu Nagasaki no Zu* which is also printed on the outside cover, and three lines of explanatory text followed by the name and address of the publisher, Ohata Bunjiyemon of Katsuyama street, Nagasaki, together with the date Horeki, 14th year, 8th month (August 1764) and an undecipherable seal in black. The map is executed in considerable detail, the names of all streets or wards, temples and government offices &c. being clearly marked in *katakana* script. It is hand coloured, the prevailing tints being red, blue, grey-green and brown. Prominent amongst the shipping in the harbour are two Dutch ships and two Chinese junks, one from Nanking and the other from Fukien respectively. Both Deshima and the Chinese factory are shown in considerable detail, and the map as a whole is certainly not without artistic merit. It was originally printed in four sheets which are joined together in the middle, as is discernible by closely examining the paper or holding it up to the light. This is the rarest of all maps of Nagasaki, and fine copies like the present one, with the original colours in a good state of preservation, are very difficult to come by.

The next oldest Toshimaya print which can be dated with certainty is a map of Nagasaki published in Annei 7 or 1778 [1]. This map presents considerable differences to the earlier Horeki one, and the modifications introduced in the 1778 version were copied or adapted in all later maps of Nagasaki. It is on almost exactly the same scale as its predecessor, there being no appreciable difference in size. In other points there are notable divergencies between the two. Both are printed in four sheets, joined together in the centre, but the colours which predominate in the Annei print are yellow, greyish-blue and black, whereby it presents a much more sober appearance than the earlier one. The inscription on the left-hand bottom corner has also swollen considerably, and in-

[1] A small reproduction of this map, together with a brief description of it will be found in Dr. Feenstra Kuiper's *Japan en de Buitenwereld*, where (p. 185), however, the date is misprinted 1773 for 1778. Titsingh seems to have brought back a copy with him to judge from the Catalogue of his collection on p. 320 of his *Illustrations of Japan*. (London, 1822). Cf. also W.Z. Mulder's article in *Cultureel Indie*, VIII, 152–6, (1946).

cludes a table of distances in *ri* [1] by land and sea to various places in Japan. The types of shipping depicted in the harbour include two Dutch vessels (one of them being towed in by Japanese oared craft) three Chinese junks from different provinces and a Siamese ship. The Japanese guard-boats and the names of daimyo to whom they belong are also given in greater detail. The general appearance of the town and the layout of the streets are practically the same in both maps, but whereas in the Horeki version, the names are written in *katakana* script, Chinese characters are substituted for this in the Annei map. On the whole it can be said that this latter is inferior to its predecessor from both an artistic and technical viewpoint, and presents a coarser appearance. Although rare, it is not nearly so difficult to find as the former. As previously noted, the Annei map is inscribed *Hishu Nagasaki Zu* signed by Ohata Bunjiyemon of Katsuyama street, Nagasaki, and dated 8th month of the seventh year of Annei or 1778.

Closely connected with this map are the two famous colour -prints of the Dutch and Chinese factories published by Toshimaya two years later in Annei 9 (1780), known as the *Deshima Oranda yashiki* (or *okuho*) *kei* and *Tojin yashiki kei* respectively. Let us take the description of Deshima first.

The title as given above, is printed in heavy type reading from left to right in the top right-hand corner. In the top left-hand corner is a seven-line inscription recording the arrival of the Hollanders at Hirado during the Keicho period, and their settlement there under the patronage of the local Daimyo, Matsuura, Hizen-no-kami. The centre of the print is occupied with a bird's-eye view of Deshima, remarkable for its picturesque accuracy of detail, and which has often been reproduced [2]. In the bottom right-hand corner is an eight-line inscription recording the construction of Deshima from reclaimed land, as a lodging place for the *Nambanijn*

[1] 1 *ri* = 2.44 miles or 3.93 k m.

[2] The earliest reproduction, somewhat modified by the European printer, is to be found in Isaac Titsingh's posthumous *Illustrations of Japan*, of which the English edition is dated London 1822. Part of the inscriptions are reproduced in a none too accurate translation on pp. 169–70 of this edition. A smaller uncoloured reproduction is also to be found in *Japan en de Buitenwereld*. Pl. I, but Dr. Feenstra Kuiper in his description of the print (p. 173–4) dates it as early XVIIIth century, whereas the real date is 1780 as we have seen.

(Portuguese) in 1636. To the right of the bridge joining Deshima to the neighbouring ward (Yedo-machi) on the mainland, is a short inscription of four lines recording the dimensions of the place. In the bottom left-hand corner is a fourth inscription mentioning the removal of the Hollanders from Hirado to Deshima in 1641, and noting the fact that they had visited Nagasaki continuously since then until the ninth year of Annei — a statement which gives the clue to the age of this print, which is otherwise undated. Finally, the name and address of the publisher are printed in larger type in the left-hand bottom corner. The original measures some 58 × 43 centimetres.

The companion print of the Chinese factory has its title *Tojin yashiki kei* near the top right-hand corner. Below this is a three-line inscription briefly recording the foundation of the Chinese factory in the first year of Genroku (1688), and stating that the Chinese had been there ever since until the ninth year of Annei (1780). The name and address of the publisher are printed in the left-hand bottom corner, as is the case with the Deshima print. The predominant colours of these prints are grey, green and yellow with a somewhat sparser use of red. The sizes are approximately the same, viz. 58 × 43 centimetres along the outer margins.

These two prints are of great interest from both a historical and artistic standpoint. As regards the latter, it is worth pointing out how the artist has contrived to get in all the characteristic detail, — the *opperhoofd* under his sunshade; the Hollander and interpreter conversing; the different types of houses; prostitutes in the upper story of one dwelling and so forth, without undue overcrowding or loss of effect. From an historical standpoint these prints are exceedingly interesting, not only as the prototypes of all subsequent large-scale views of the Dutch and Chinese factories, but because they were the first recorded Nagasaki-e to be brought to Europe. Copies of them were obtained by Isaac Titsingh who was in Japan just at the time of their publication ,and who was able to procure them despite the ban maintained by the Shogunal government on all maps or views of towns and cities. Titsingh brought these prints to Europe in 1796, and after his death they were published (albeit in a somewhat bowdlerized form, with the inscriptions removed and printed separately in translation) amongst the plates included in his posthumous work *Illustrations of Japan.* The originals of these prints are exceedingly rare, especially that of Deshima. I have a copy of the Chinese factory, but could not procure a single example of the other during a residence of over three years in Japan.

We now come to an exceedingly interesting series of Toshimaya prints, which for want of a better title, I may term the *Schellach* type, because the representation of a Dutch Indiaman of that name forms a prominent feature of all of them. The origin and ramifications of this type of print have been dealt with in a recent article by the present writer on which the following remarks are based [1], and to which the reader is referred for proof of the statements made below. In chronological sequence, these prints may be described as follows, —

    1. *c.* 1770–1779. The Annei-period print of Amsterdam harbour, with two Dutch Indiamen flying V.O.C. flags in the foreground, that on the right-hand having the name *Schllaak* (*sic* for *Schellach* [2]) on the stern.

This print has no title or explanation attached, and no indication of who was the publisher; but it is recognizable as a Toshimaya production by the style, and by its obvious association with the later prints of this series described below. The scene is easily identifiable as Amsterdam harbour, by the two inscriptions *MUYDER POORT. LA PORTE DE MUYDEN* (in the centre), and *LEYDTSE POORT. La Porte de Leyden* (at the top). Other noteworthy features are the exceptional size of the print and the vividness of some of the colours used, especially red and black, which with brown and grey form the predominant tints. A comparison of this print with contemporary Chinese wood-cuts, reveals beyond all doubt that it has very strong traces of Chinese influence.

---

[1] *Rin Shihei and his Picture of a Dutch East-India ship,* 1782, printed on pp. 45–66 of the *Transactions of the Asiatic of Japan,* Tokyo, 1932.

[2] Also spelt *Schellag.* The name was derived from a manor-house in Zeeland. To the details about the *Schellag* East Indiaman of 1736 given on p. 55 of the essay quoted in the last note, must be added the fact that she was taken by the French ship *Kersain* in 1749 and brought first to Pondicherry and then to Mauritius, after part of her cargo of Japanese gold and copper bullion had been taken out of her. She was subsequently restored to the Hollanders after a long and acrimonious correspondence between Batavia and Pondicherry on the subject. Cf. the documents printed in *Kron. Hist. Gen.* Deelen 28, 29 & 30.

PLATE VIII

MUYDER POORT. LA PORTE DE MUYDEN.

From the original in the author's collection

Nagasaki (*Toshimaya*) colour-print of two East-Indiamen in Amsterdam harbour, *circa* 1779

Especially the towers, with their pagoda-like appearance betray the hand of a Celestial artist. It is therefore most probable that the original was either executed by a Chinese artist at Nagasaki after some European copper-engraving, or, more likely, copied by Toshimaya from a Chinese version of the Dutch original. Judging by the type of shipping, dress of the crews, and the European lettering in Dutch and French, this original was probably an engraving in some mid-XVIIIth century pictorial work on the United Provinces, but efforts to trace it have so far failed. The print was made from two separate blocks, upper and lower, which joined together in the centre some few inches above the *Muyderpoort* inscription. This and the following prints are so different in size and appearance from the ordinary Nagasaki-e, that they were probably made for some specific purpose, and not merely for sale to ordinary tourists. Reliable tradition, and some more definite historical facts, connect them with the name of the celebrated patriotic writer Rin (or Hayashi) Shihei, and though this connection is rather doubtful in the case of this present print, yet it may well date from the year 1777, when Hayashi Shihei paid his first visit to Nagasaki, and when the sight of it may have inspired him to publish the later *Schellach* prints. In any case, this is one of the rarest of all Nagasaki-e, and so far as I know there are only two complete and perfect copies in existence, one of which belonged to the late General J. C. Pabst, and the other to Mr. Ikenaga of Kobe. I myself possess an example of the lower or *Muyderpoort* section, whilst Professor Kuroda apparently possesses the missing upper or *Leydtse poort* half. Exhaustive enquiries during a residence of more than three years in Japan failed to bring to light any more examples, whether complete or not (see Plate opposite).

    2. *c.* 1782. The Tenmei-period print of the East-Indiaman *Schellach*.

    There are two variants of this print, which differ only in the inscription, and both were obviously published at about the same time, though only one is actually dated. We will take the latter first.

    a) This print measures 60 × 80 centimetres and depicts af XVIIIth century Dutch East-India ship with the name SCHLLAAK on the stern. There is no title or heading but the upper half of the print is occupied by a long inscription written with a *fudé* or native writing brush, describing Holland and its inhabitants, and giving details of Dutch commercial relations with Nagasaki [1].

One at least of the four copies known (that in the Imperial Housebold Museum at Ueno, Tokyo) bears the seal of Rin Shihei and Toshimaya Denkichi as publishers of the print. It is not clear whether this Denkichi was the same person as Ohata Bunjiyemon, founder of the firm, or a son or relative, but anyhow the print is thus identified with the Toshimaya publishing house. The print is made from one block, and the principal colours used are red, blue, brown and black. It seems quite certain that this print was published by Hayashi Shihei who paid his second visit to Nagasaki in 1782, for circulation amongst his friends and acquaintances in order to induce them to subscribe funds for the publication of his great work on coast defence — the *Kaikoku Heidan* — but it is not quite clear on what terms Toshimaya printed it, or why this particular ship was selected. But it is obvious that there was some connection between this Tenmei print of the *Schellach* and the Annei print of Amsterdam harbour, since not only does the *Schellach* figure in both, under the guise of SCHLLAAK, but even the inscription MUYDERPOORT. LA PORTE DE MUYDEN in the earlier print, is reproduced in a corrupted form MUYDER POORT LA[PO] on one of the flags of the Tenmei *Schellach*. Many other details such as the red coats and costumes of the crew, V.O.C. inscription on the flags and so forth are the same in both cases. Needless to say this Tenmei-2 print is exceedingly rare, even if not quite so scarce as its Annei predecessor. Of the four existing copies which are known to me, I will cite those of General J. C. Pabst, Ueno Museum, and Imperial University Kyoto, as the ones which I have actually examined. The only difference between them (other than natural variations in the degree of colouring in the flags and general state of preservation) is the absence, or otherwise, of the seal declaring the work to have been originated by Rin Shihei and Toshimaya, at the end of the long manuscript inscription.

[1] A full translation of this inscription will be found on pp. 177–179 of Appendix II, *infra*.

b) Oranda Sen no Zu; or Picture of a Hollander Ship.

This is an undated variant of (a), described above, but must date from the same year Tenmei 2 (1782) or thereabouts. Perhaps indeed it is the older of the two. The ship, as also the colouring and dimensions of this print are the same as in the dated print, but it is without the long inscription written by Hayashi Shihei. In place thereof, is the title *Oranda Sen no Zu* recorded above, and the Dutch words, *Son, Maan, Sterre* written in a bold flowing hand with a writing brush across the top of the print, and with the Sino-Japanese equivalents of these words placed above. In the top right-hand corner, on the left of the title, is a short five-line inscription giving the dimensions of the ship and brief statistical details concerning its equipment and crew. On the left side is a short table of distances in *ri* from Japan to some nine European and Asiatic countries including Holland, England, Portugal, Madagascar, Sumatra and Jacatra (Batavia) [1]. As is the case with the other prints of this series, the colours on the flags and coats of the crew, in which red and grey predominate, are applied by hand, whereas the black and brown tints which form the basic shades for the ship's hull are printed from woodblocks. This variant is even rarer than the dated version, and apart from my own copy (which is reproduced in the frontispiece) I only know of one other, namely that in the possession of the Van Renselaer Bowier family at Amsterdam [2].

3. *Oranda Sen Zusetsu; or Pictorial Explanation of Hollander ship.* [1790].

This is the third oldest version of the *Schellach* print, and published in Kwansei 2 (1790). It bears a close resemblance to the Tenmei-2 print described in paragraph 2 (a) above, but this Kwansei print is longer and narrower, measuring *c.* 53 × 99 cm. There are minor but perceptible differences in the details of the waves, the ship's rigging, and in the inscription, which last is practically identical with that of eight years earlier save for the date. The authorship of the in-

---

[1] These inscriptions are translated in full on pp. 62–3 of my article *op.cit.*

[2] This last example was reproduced and described by Mr. Balbian Verster in an article published in *Elsevier's Maandschrift* for April 1914, and in another printed in the *Mariner's Mirror* for that year. Both articles contain a few mistakes which are rectified in my later essay. My copy was lost when the Japanese occupied Hong-ong in 1941–45.

scription is likewise ascribed to Hayashi Shihei who published his great work, the *Kaikoku Heidan* at Sendai in the
following year. Its existence would seem to demonstrate that
the earlier prints of Tenmei-2 had proved popular enough to
have been sold out and the stocks exhausted. This was apparently the case with the Kwansei version too, since, as far
as is known, only two copies have survived to the present day,
of which one is in the collection of Mr. Ikenaga and figures in
his Catalogue [1].

The popularity of this *Schellach* type of print (*Oranda Sen
no Zu*, or *Oranda Sen Zusetzu* as most subsequent reproductions were headed), is strikingly proved by the numerous and
increasingly bastardized versions thereof, published from the
end of the XVIIIth century onwards. These are at first easily
recognizable as they retain the name SCHLLAAK, or a
corruption of it, on the stern, whilst some of the figures
of the crew, inscriptions on the flags and so forth are the
same as in the Tenmei prints. They are all on a smaller scale,
and as the XIXth century progresses they become increasingly coarse, until about 1850 the original becomes
practically unrecognizable with a paddle-wheel and other
modern inventions attached to it. Rin Shihei's inscription
also disappears after Kwansei-2, but the table of distances
given in the Tenmei variant described under 2 (b) above,
persists down to the bitter end. Readers who wish to see the
beginning of this gradual transformation can do so by examining the Plates reproduced on p. 7 of Mr. Nagami's *Zoku
Nagasaki Hangwa Shu*; though there are many later variants
not reproduced in that work.

Whilst we are on the subject of Hayashi Shihei and his
connection with the *Schellach* type of print published by
Toshimaya, we may find space to mention another type of
print with which his name is associated, namely the *Oranda Jin
Enkai no Zu* or *Picture of Hollanders' banquet*, one of which, in
the collection General J. C. Pabst, is of special interest.
The print is headed in the top right-hand corner *Oranda Jin
Enkai no Zu*. The inscription below may be translated as
follows, — "Explanation of this Picture; Instead of rice,

[1] Cf. Plate 156 of Vol. II. A smaller reproduction is given by Professor Kuroda in
his *Seiyo no Eikyo wo uketaru Nihongwa* (P. 11).

they use food made from roasted wheat, with meat and fowls as relish, followed by fruits. For drink, they have a kind of red coloured wine. Their method of eating is quite different from ours. The dishes are served up separately one after an-other." The two lines in the bottom left-hand corner read in translation. "Drawn and described by Rin Shihei of Sendai in the autumn of Tenmei 2" (1782). These inscriptions as also the colouring of the print are applied by hand (? by Shihei himself), and only the general outlines of the chairs, figures, and so forth have been engraved from wood blocks. It might be be added that the empty chair on the left is traditionally said to be that occupied by Shihei himself on the occasions of his visits to the Dutch Factory; it being presumed that he left it unoccupied in the picture for fear lest the portrayal of his feasting with the Red-haired barbarians would bring down the wrath of the Bakufu on his head; for any Japanese, other than the official interpreters, who were on friendly terms with foreigners were liable to incur the suspicion of the Shogunal authorities, as indeed did Hayashi Shihei himself a decade later.

Modified issues and reprints of this print will be found in the oft-quoted books of Mr. Nagami and Professor Kuroda [1]. The inscription and date by Hayashi Shihei are omitted in all of them, and there is usually substituted a heading HOLLANDER inscribed in capital letters on a scroll, and flanked by a barely decipherable rigmarole in European script which can be recognized in the better printed examples as intended for the phrase *Deze print is zuiver gedruckt*. Two typical prints of this type are reproduced on Plates 13 and 14 of Professor Kuroda's work. At first sight they appear identic-al, but closer scrutiny immediately reveals curious differ-ences, such as the monogram on the back of the empty chair, which is A in one type and H in the other; in one case the dress of the Javanese boy on the right is of flowered pattern and he is carrying a dish of eggs, whilst in the other print his costume is of striped material and he is carrying an ox's head on his tray; in one case, both the Dutchman facing the reader have hats on, whilst in the other, one of them is

[1] The print of a Dutch party reproduced in Plate 31 of Kuroda's work has nothing in common with the Deshima party depicted by Hayashi Shihei and Toshimaya, but is obviously copied directly from some Dutch print.

bare-headed, and so on. Finally it should be stated that Ha-yashi Shihei is supposed to have distributed this print in the same way as that of the *Schellach* in order to obtain funds for the publication of his *Kaikoku Heidan*.

The reader may have noticed that in none of these prints does the name of the publisher occur, but the presumption that they are the work of Toshimaya is very strong. Not only are they in his style, and the colours used closely resemble those employed by him, but we know that Shihei's print of the *Schellach* was engraved and published by him this same year, so it seems obvious that this "Dutch party" type must be his work too. In the same style, and consequently, in all probability, likewise the work of Toshimaya, is the print of a Hollander reproduced on Plate 186 of Vol II of the Ikenaga Catalogue. It will be noticed that the HOLLANDER heading is the same as in the Dutch party print, whilst at the bottom is the phrase *Deze print is zuiver gedrukt* which likewise figures in the former. The relative clearness of this inscription together with the general appearance of the print, point to the fact that it is older than the party print, and we shall probably not err greatly in placing it in the Annei period 1771–9, or even earlier, during the closing years of Horeki *c.* 1760. There is a very similar print of the JUFFROUW VAN HOLLAD (sic) dating from about the same time, but whereas the man with his Javanese retainer has some appearance of having been drawn from life, the gro-tesque appearance of the woman is irresistably comic. The Japanese artist who was obviously copying some unfamiliar European engraving, has produced a sort of Watteau shep-herdess whose crook is metamorphosed into a *yari* or Japanese lance, and the bouquet in her left hand transformed into a sort of glorified cabbage. Grotesque as they are, however, these prints are very rare, and the student will do well to study the examples reproduced in the works of Kuroda (Plates 15 & 16) and Nagami (Plates 2, 6 and 8).

None of these prints are signed or dated, but they were probably published by Toshimaya at varying periods during the last quarter of the XVIIIth century. All of them are rare and the order of their precedence and most other facts about them have yet to be studied in detail.

After the publication of the *Oranda Sen Zusetzu* by Toshimaya in 1790, there is a gap of more than twenty years until
his next signed and dated production in Bunkwa 8 (1811).
This is the representation of a Korean ambassadorial procession, but, as it has no connection with Holland or the Hollanders, we shall merely refer the interested reader to Professor Kuroda's description and reproduction of it on p. 69
and Plate 17 of his work. We have neither time nor space to
describe any of the other prints published by Toshimaya
during the first half of the XIXth century, but it may be
mentioned that amongst them is a print of Mevrouw Cock
Blomhoff with her European nurse and baby, dated 1817,
which trio formed such a popular subject for the Nagasaki
artists and print dealers at the time. The chief colours employed in this last-named print are indigo, violet and yellow.
Professor Kuroda makes some interesting observations on the
technical similarities between the colours and style of this
print with that of the Chosen (Korean) embassy published six
years before. The last dated print published by Toshimaya
was a map of Nagasaki printed in Bunsei 4 (1821), and it
seems that the firm petered out altogether a few years later.

In spite of a somewhat inglorious end, the firm of Toshimaya during the fifty odd years of its existence might justly
be regarded as having produced the most interesting and the
most original Nagasaki-e. Especially is this true of the earlier
years of its existence, during what one might term the *incuna-
bula* period of Nagasaki colour-prints of before 1790. In the
view of the present writer at any rate, the most valuable and
interesting *Nagasaki-e*, whether regarded from an historical
or an artistic standpoint, are those published by Ohata Bunjiyemon, master of the Toshimaya in more senses than one,
between 1770 and 1790.

(iii) *Bunkindo*. The colour-prints published by this firm are
in many ways the most typical of all Nagasaki-e, whether on
account of their number or of the variety of their designs. The
most flourishing period of the Bunkindo was during the first
four decades of the XIXth century, and the earliest print
bearing the stamp of this firm which can be dated with
certainty, is the map of Nagasaki published in the second

year of Kyowa (1802). As this map has been often reproduced it is not necessary to do more than note its most striking characteristics here [1].

The map is entitled *Shinkoku Hizen Nagasaki Zu*, or *Newly engraved map of Nagasaki in Hizen*. On comparison with the Annei 7 (1778) map published by Toshimaya, it is obvious that it is based on this latter, and it is drawn on the same scale, although the measurements of the outside margins are a trifle less. The colouring also resembles that of the earlier print, though the tints employed in the Kyowa copy (in which blue, yellow and grey-green predominate) are deeper and better preserved. The tables of sea and land distances from Nagasaki to various places in Japan (mostly neighbouring towns in Kyushu) are also retained, but two innovations are added. These are distinguishing signs which mark the *yashi-ki* of the Daimyo (▮) many of whom, especially the Kyushu ones, maintained houses in the city for commercial trans-actions, and the dwellings of the local aldermen or *machi-toshiyori* (▲). As in the Annei print, two Dutch ships are depicted, but the one being towed in is firing a salute, whilst the Chinese junks are reduced to two (one from Fukien and the other from Nanking, both having the names of their ports written in characters instead of in *kana* as in the Annei version); the Siamese vessel has been omitted, or rather transform-ed into one of the Chinese junks, namely that from Fukien. The name and address of the publishing firm, together with the date, Kyowa second year, sixth month (July, 1802) are printed in the bottom left-hand corner. As is the case with the Annei map, and in contrast to Toshimaya's map of Hore-ki 14, none of the colours are applied by hand, but all are printed from wood-blocks. Another point worthy of notice, is the border to the title *Shinkoku Hizen Nagasaki Zu* printed on the outer folding cover. This border contains represen-tations of various things used by the Dutch and Chinese, such as gin bottle, wine cup, pipe, trumpet, Chinese hat and

---

[1] Besides the small scale reproductions in the works of Msesrs. Kuroda, Nagami, and Ikenaga, *op. cit.*, there is a facsimile reproduction, with the table of distances omitted and with all the street names translated into English, included in Paske Smith's *Japanese Traditions of Christianity*, (Kobe, 1930) p. 132. This reproduction also figures in the same editor's *Western Barbarians in Japan and Formosa* (Kobe, 1930) and his edition of Raffles' *Report on Japan in 1812–1816* (Kobe, 1929).

fan, &c. There was a smaller edition of this print published by Bunkindo in the same year, but with considerable differences in the arrangement of the shipping, omission of the distance table and so forth.

Close on the heels of these Kyowa maps, come the prints relating to Rezanov's embassy to Japan published by Bunkindo in Bunkwa 1 (1804), and which depict the ambassador either alone, or with various members of his suite, and are provided with brief explanatory inscriptions. These prints are therefore highly interesting contemporary sources for the study of Rezanov's abortive mission to Nagasaki, but as they have no direct connection with the Hollanders, we will do no more than allude to the fact of their existence [1].

Although the earliest known *dated* production of Bunkindo was published in 1802, yet Professor Kuroda advances strong arguments in favour of the attribution to this firm of a number of undated prints which are obviously of earlier origin. These include two separate representations of a Hollander and his Javanese slave (in the approved stylized version affected by the Nagasaki print masters), two complementary ones of a Chinaman of the Tsing or Manchu dynasty, and prints of a Dutch ship of the *Schellach* type, and of a Chinese junk. Professor Kuroda ascribes his attribution of these prints to the Bunkindo firm on technical grounds connected with the colours used and their application. The same eminent authority dates the Chinese portraits from about the middle of the Kwansei period or *c.* 1795, those of the Hollander from the Tenmei period (1780–1790), and the prints of the Dutch and Chinese ships from the beginning of the Tenmei period, or even earlier. To the comparatively untrained eye of the present writer, the prints of the Hollander seem to resemble rather those of the Hariya or Toshimaya schools than that of Bunkindo; although it is of course quite possible that the latter copied his predecessors more closely at this early period than in later years when the firm had developed a definite style of its own. The print of the Dutch ship is

---

[1] These prints are reproduced in figures 21–3 of Professor Kuroda's work and briefly described on p. 71 of the same.

Good accounts of Rezanov's mission to Nagasaki will be found in Doeff's *Herinneringen* and in Vol. III of Murdoch's *History of Japan*.

clearly a version of the *Shellach* print (compare the details of crew, flags, ship's hull and explanatory inscription), so that it can hardly be earlier than and is more likely to date from after 1790. Two versions of this print are known, of which Mr. Nagami reproduced both on Plate 7 of his album *Zoku Nagasaki Hangwa shu*, and Professor Kuroda one in Plate 29 of his work. The one that is reproduced by both authorities is ascribed by the former to Toshimaya and by the latter to Bunkindo. Where two such eminent connoisseurs disagree it is perhaps presumptuous for a foreigner to venture his opinion, but the present writer firmly believes that both prints should be ascribed to Toshimaya, owing to their obvious derivation from the *Schellach*, whose name still survives on the stern in one case.

Nevertheless, apart from the controversial nature of these prints, it is clear that Bunkindo had begun publication before 1802, as is proved by the existence of a print of a Chinese family bearing the seal of this firm and which is of an undoubtedly older type than its XIXth century productions (cf. Plate I of Mr. Nagami's album *op. cit.*) [1]. Of a more familiar type is the series of prints representing Dutch and Chinese shipping, either singly or in combination, which was begun by Bunkindo in the early years of the Bunkwa period about 1803. Most of these prints are readily identifiable by the name of the firm which is usually attached to them in some form or other, though they are very rarely dated. Their many types and subdivisions are too numerous to describe here, but generally speaking the older types are more elaborate, and have lengthier explanatory inscriptions. Some of them are headed in Dutch, HOLLANDSCHE SCHIP, and the influence of the *Schellach* type can still be detected in the inscriptions of the earliest ones which are copied *verbatim* from the 1782 *Oranda Sen no Zu* described above (pp. 82–3). The principal colours used are the so-called *Taisha* red, yellow clay, and pale blue; and a good idea of this type of Bunkindo print can be obtained from the examples reproduced in Plates 162–167 of the Ikenaga Catalogue.

[1] There is a colour-print of a Hollander and cassowry sometimes met with, which is also one of the older Bunkindo prints to judge by its general appearance, and may well date from the Kwansei period, or even earlier.

Another type of this firm's publications which demands a brief notice in this connection, is the print of a Dutch-style party, or rather debauch judging by the abandoned attitudes of the participants and the number of empty bottles depicted. This type of print is usually entitled *Komo Jin Koraku no Zu*, and one of the earliest examples has a manuscript title added in Dutch *Afteeken van vroolijkheid der Hollanders* probably by some interpreter. A cursory examination of this type of "party" print reveals that it is quite different from the Shihei-Toshimaya type of print depicting a banquet at Deshima as described above (p. 84–5); for Bunkindo's version is clearly based on some European engraving, as is evidenced *inter alia* by the presence of white women, and not taken from life like those of the earlier Toshimaya series. The date of the oldest print of this series is uncertain, but it may go back to the end of the XVIIIth century. There is a modified reprint of the Bunsei (1818–29) period, which has not got the European heading [1].

Amongst the more notable colour-prints published by this firm whilst at the height of its productivity, we may make special mention of those depicting an elephant and camel imported in Bunkwa 10 (1813) and Bunsei 4 (1821) respectively. The Japanese passion for detail is further exemplified in the information which is given on the prints concerning the sizes of these animals, the amount of food they consumed and so forth. Some idea of the varied subjects which contributed to form the prolific list of Bunkindo productions during the early nineteenth century, may be gained from the following typical examples. Map of Kyushu dated 1813; Chinese ships of four varieties; Dutchmen, whether singly or in groups; Chinese religious procession on the occasion of their "Bosa" festival in Nagasaki; the Colossus of Rhodes; early steam vessels; Dutch warship *Palembang*; and last but by no means least, the very interesting series of prints depicting the visit of Kapitein-ter-Zee Koops in 1844. This naval officer brought a letter from King Willem II to the Shogun, and the ceremonial procession with a drum, fife and trumpet band on the occasion of the delivery of this missive to the local authorities at Tateyama, seems to have inspired a regular

[1] For examples of this type of print cf. Ikenaga's Catalogue. Vol. II plates 187–9.

series of Bunkindo prints. The earlier ones are relatively accurate, and attention is chiefly devoted to the French horns and other unfamiliar instruments carried by the bandsmen. As is the case with most of the subjects which originally served to inspire Nagasaki-e, this comparative accuracy soon gave way to an impressionistic riot, in which the fertile imagination of the Japanese artist and engraver indulged in an orgy of elephants, chariots, sedan-chairs and what they were pleased to consider other necessary adjuncts to any proper "Red-haired Barbarian" procession. The climax of absurdity was reached in one print which depicts the gallant Captain Koops (complete with cocked hat and grasping the inevitable pipe) seated astride an elephant in the midst of a motley crowd of bandsmen sporting drums, French horns, trumpets and even an umbrella! Bunkindo prints are very numerous about the Kaei period (1838–1853) and the years immediately following, but their artistic merit declined proportionately, and the later productions of this firm are crude in the extreme. The increasing influence of the Yedo Ukiyoe on the colour and technique of Nagasaki-e is very obvious in the Bunkindo prints published from the end of the Tempo period (c. 1840) onwards; but the subjects of these prints continue to be taken exclusively from local scenes connected with foreign intercourse.

(iv) *Yamatoya.* The last great publishing-house of Nagasaki-e, whether from an artistic or chronological standpoint, was the firm of Yamatoya which flourished from the end of the Tempo era (1843) until about 1860. In style and general appearance, as also in the colours used, the Yamatoya prints have much in common with the later Bunkindo productions, from which they are sometimes difficult to distinguish in the absence of a seal or stamp indicating their origin. Like the contemporary Bunkindo prints, the Yamatoya-e are strongly influenced by the Yedo Ukiyoe schools as regards colouring and technique, though the subjects selected continue to be of exclusively local interest. Though the life of this firm was comparatively short, (only about twenty years), it produced some notable prints during this time, and from a numerical point of view its productions rank second only to those of the Bunkindo.

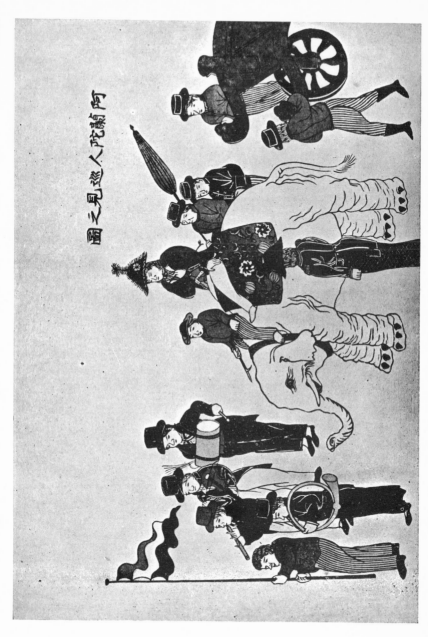

圖之見人巡陀阿

From the original in the collection of General J. C. Pabst

Nagasaki (Bunkindo) colour-print inspired by Captain Koops' mission in 1844

PLATE IX

The name of this firm is closely connected with Isono Bunsai who was one of its masters (if not its actual founder) and the author-illustrator of the *Nagasaki-Miyage* published in 1847. Bunsai had studied under one of the Ukiyoe masters of Yedo; hence his work is strongly influenced thereby, and though it gains something in technical skill yet loses some of the fresh spontaneity which characterizes the earlier if cruder Nagasaki-e. Another famous artist closely connected with the Yamatoya was Kawara or Kawahara Keiga, who painted portraits of Doeff, Cock Blomhoff and Siebold, and whose work as a portrait painter has considerable merit. Amongst the most interesting productions of Yamatoya, whether from an artistic or historical standpoint, are the print of Mevrouw Cock Blomhoff with her child and nurse, and the seven prints representing Admiral Putiatine's mission of 1853, recalling the earlier Bunkindo representation of Kapitein-ter-Zee Koops' arrival in 1844, of which several versions are extant, and which have been briefly described on the previous page. The Yamatoya series is much the better production from all points of view. Space must also be found for the mention of Bunsai's portrait of the nineteen year-old bride of Mr. Hubert de Villeneuve, who came to Nagasaki in 1829, but, like Mevrouw Blomhoff, she was not allowed to remain in Japan. There are two versions of her portrait, both very rare, which differ slightly in size as also in the length of the explanatory inscription in the top right-hand corner. It is to be presumed that these prints are contemporary with Mrs. de Villeneuve's arrival or nearly so, and thus antedate the cruder reproduction on p. 16 of the *Nagasaki Miyage*. The majority of the Yamatoya prints are distinguished by the seal, which usually takes the form of the character for "great" enclosed in a gourd-shaped oval. For the rest, a good idea of the style of these prints can be obtained from the example here reproduced (Pl. X) and those in Mr. Nagami's Album (Plates 25, 26 & 31), and in Mr. Ikenaga's Catalogue (Plates 168–175), and in vol. I of Mr. Mody's.

Other Nagasaki-e. It is not necessary to do more than briefly mention the existence of the remaining publishing-houses of Nagasaki-e, since none of them can be compared in importance with the long-lived and enterprising firms of Toshima-ya, Bunkindo or Yamatoya. The following are the names of some of them, Ogiya, Imamiya, and Wataya. Most of them flourished during the late period of Nagasaki-e c. 1850–1860, and thus their subjects include not only Dutch, Chinese and Russians but also English and Americans. The Imamiya dates from 1802 at least, as it then published a map of Nagasaki, evidently in rivalry with the better known Bunkindo one of the same year. For the rest they do not differ much from the later Bunkindo and Yamatoya productions although they are usually less carefully finished. Typical specimens are given in Plates 176–8 of Mr. Ikenaga's Catalogue (*Hosaibankwa Daihokan*).

From what has been stated in the foregoing paragraphs and from the reproductions given, it will be seen that the so called Nagasaki-e are by no means deficient in either artistic merit or historical interest. Even if they cannot compete in the former respect with the average Ukiyoe print of the period, yet their historical significance is probably greater. At any rate their continued, and at times prolific, existence for a period of over a century is one more additional piece of evidence to prove that Japan was not nearly so isolated or separated from foreign contacts as some historians would still have us believe. As has been said, they were purely a form of popular art (with the possible exception of the prints made for Hayashi Shihei), and their relative inferiority and cheapness enabled them to circulate freely amongst the ordinary townspeople. Being sold chiefly to visitors and tourists who came to Nagasaki, they were spread by this means throughout the length and breadth of Japan. It would of course be idle to pretend that they exercised any vital influence on the gradually broadening interest in things European which went far to prepare the way for the Meiji restoration; but it is undeniable that their mere existence contributed something towards creating and maintaining that interest, and in this respect they may claim a modest share in laying the foundations of Modern Japan [1].

[1] Nothing has been said in this essay about the influence of purely technical methods (such as a correct representation of perspective) derived from the West, which is evident in the works of Maruyama Okyo, Shiba Kokan and in some prints of the Yedo Ukiyoe masters. For a discussion of this influence see the first two sections of Professor Kuroda's book *op. cit.*

PLATE X   P. 94

From the original in the collection of General J. C. Pabst

Nagasaki *(Yamatoya)* colour-print of Mevrouw Cock Blomhoff, her child and nurse,
circa 1818

II. *Paintings in oils and water-colours*

(a) *Artists of the Nagasaki schools.* Painting in European style and with European materials (oils) dates from the time of the Portuguese in Japan, when the Jesuit seminaries at Nagasaki, Arima, and elsewhere in Kyushu contained quite a number of competent artists in this branch, both Japanese pupils as European teachers. The mural and other decorations of the local Catholic churches were all done by native acolytes after the European manner, and in a way which excited the admiration of all beholders. Needless to say, the subjects of this style of Western painting were exclusively religious, and as such, this art is believed to have become extinct on the extermination of Christianity by the Bakufu during the first half of the XVIIth century.

The foregoing statement as to the exclusively religious *motifs* of this Japanese-Jesuit (if one may so term it) art must be qualified as to one of its leading exponents, namely the famous or perhaps infamous Yamada Emonsaku. This man, reputed to have been a skilled painter in oils, was involved on the rebels' side in the Shimabara rebellion of 1637–8, though apparently involuntarily. Detected in the act of treacherously communicating with Matsudaira Izu-no-kami Nobutsuna, commander of the besieging Shogunal forces, Yamada was imprisoned in Hara castle; but his life was saved by the fall of the fortress in April 1638, when he was one of the very few, according to some accounts indeed the sole survivor whose life was spared. He is traditionally alleged to have received official permission for continuing to exercise his art as an oil-painter, but if so, it is clear that his subsequent works must have been of a secular and not of a religious character. No work of his which can be identified with absolute certainty has survived, but a painting of a European lady in late sixteenth century costume playing a guitar, which is commonly attributed to him, was exhibited at Tokyo in 1930, being subsequently acquired by Mr. Ikenaga. The painting, though much damaged by the ravages of time, certainly looks like dating from the early seventeenth century, and whether it is

actually the work of Yamada Emonsaku himself or not, it
gives a good idea of his style [1].

It is commonly alleged by most writers on the subject of
European influence in Japanese art, that the art of painting in
oils was lost after the extinction of Christianity in the middle
of the seventeenth century, and that it was not revived until
the fresh impetus towards Western arts and sciences which
accompanied the activities of the Dutch scholars or *Rangakusha* made itself felt during the last quarter of the eighteenth
century. Nevertheless, as Professor G. Kuroda has pointed
out in a recent work on this subject [2], it is doubtful whether this
view is tenable, despite the almost total lack of any Japanese
oil painting which can be dated between 1650 and 1750.
Apart from the fact that it seems unlikely that Yamada Emonsaku would have allowed his art to die with him, there are
categorical if brief references to the existence of oil paintings
in Japan between the two above-mentioned dates. The clear-
est of these references we owe to the invaluable Nishikawa
Joken, who alludes in his *Nagasaki Yawagusa* of 1720 to the
existence of oil-painters at Nagasaki in both the *Namban*
(Portuguese) and *Komo* (Red-hair or Hollander) styles.
Unfortunately he does not specify the difference between
them nor give the names of any artists; but it seems most
probable that these latter merely copied works imported
by the Dutch, as we have several references to the importation of pictures by the Hollanders during the XVIIIth
century [3].

As Dr. Feenstra Kuiper has pointed out in his *Japan en de
Buitenwereld in de achttiende eeuw*, the influence exercised by
the Hollanders on the pictorial art of Old Japan, can be divided into two forms, which however cannot always readily
be distinguished, —

1. The motives and subjects afforded by the Hollanders

---

[1] Reproduced in *Hosaibankwa Daihokan*. An excellent study of Japanese-Jesuit
art by John E. McCall, *Early Jesuit Art in the Far East* in *Artibus Asiae*, Vol X–XI
(1947–8) with numerous excellent illustrations, may be recommended to readers.

[2] Prof. G. Kuroda, *Nagasaki-kei Yogwa* (Osaka, 1932) which supersedes all previous
works on the subject such as Mr. T. Nagami's *Nagasaki no Bijitsu-shi* and forms the
basis of most of what follows.

[3] Cf. Feenstra Kuiper, *Japan en de Buitenwereld*, p. 282. Dr. Kuiper misspells Yamada Emonsaku as Emasuken, be it noted in passing.

themselves, or by the articles they imported, as themes for the Japanese artist.

2. In the technical sphere, such as in the introduction of new and fresh materials, or in the innovation of hitherto unknown rules like those of linear perspective and so forth. For a further study of this question, it is convenient to divide the Japanese students of Western Art into two schools or groups, — those who learnt and practised this art in Nagasaki, and those who did so elsewhere in Japan. We will take the former first.

Araki Genkei and Araki Genyu. Although as we have seen, the Nagasaki writer, Nishikawa Joken, alludes to the existence of painters in oils after the Dutch style in his native place during the late seventeenth century, neither the names nor the works of any such are known until the advent of the Araki family in the later part of the eighteenth century. Araki Genkei was an official painter and art critic of some renown who died in Kwansei 11 (1799) but the only surviving picture of his which shows any traces of foreign influence is a peculiar *kakemono* (hanging scroll) in the collection of Mr. Ikenaga, depicting the stern and poop of a Dutch ship, with figures of some of the crew in late XVIIth century costume, and which has little to commend it except for the unusual viewpoint [1]. His adopted son, *Araki Genyu*, is said in contemporary records to have been a skilled painter in oils, but as no such painting of his has hitherto come to light, his merits in this respect remain uncertain. Genyu died early in the XIXth century, and his chief claim to fame resolves itself into the fact that he was the teacher of his son,

Ishizaki Yushi, with whom we are on firmer ground. Ishizaki Yushi (a reproduction of whose signature and seal will be found on p. 24 of Professor Kuroda's work) was a longlived and busy artist, with consequently a large and varied output of works. Contemporary chroniclers assert that in addition to being a skilled painter in oils, he also learnt the art of making mirrors and looking-glasses with quicksilver from foreigners, which would seem to imply that he was indebted for progress in his art to the direct instruction of some Hol-

---

[1] Paintings by or ascribed to the Araki and other Nagasaki painters will be found illustrated in Vol. II of the Mody *Catalogue* (Kobe, 1939).

lander(s), as much as to what he had acquired from his father.
Most of his work was produced in the Bunkwa-Tempo eras
(c. 1800–1840) and includes several pictures of Dutch and Chinese shipping, one of the former being dated Tempo 4 (1833).
Besides the adoption of oils as a medium of work, he also
introduced perspective into his views after the European
manner. Some idea of his style may be gained from examining
the pictures of his reproduced in Professor Kuroda's excellent
Nagasaki-kei Yogwa, though none of these (unless it be the
one reproduced on Plate 12 of that work), are in oils. These
include a painting on silk of the elephant imported in Bunkwa
10 (1813) with its mahout, and a painting of a camel imported by the Dutch in Bunsei 4 (1821). This last is one of a
series of paintings depicting various birds, beasts, and other
objects of interest brought by the Dutch or Chinese to Japan
during the early XIXth century, and was formerly in the possession of the Takagi family, one of whom was then *Daikwan*
or Shogunal commissioner at Nagasaki. Yushi seems to have
been connected with this family in some way, and hence had
opportunities of visiting the Dutch and Chinese factories,
which resulted in his representations of things foreign being
more accurate than is usually the case [1].

Another relic from his brush is a *makimono*, or long scroll,
depicting the mutinous crew of a Portuguese brig bound from
Timor to Macau, who had murdered their officers and then
drifted to the Goto islands, whence they were brought to Nagasaki in 1801 [2]. The actual painting is dated two years later and
gives the name, age, and country of origin of each member of the
crew, amongst the former being clearly recognizable Portuguese appellations such as Antonio, Caetano, Agostinho and
Maria. In addition to his own son, Ishizaki Yushi, Araki Genyu
had an adopted son who took the name of Araki Jogen and
likewise achieved some renown as a painter in oils.

Araki Jogen, a facsimile of whose signature will be found
on p. 46 of Professor Kuroda's *Nagasaki-kei-Yogwa*, became

---

[1] Other drawings of his in the same (native) style will be found in the *Nagasaki
Meisho Zue*, of which work he was the illustrator. Some of the woodcuts are reproduced
in Dr. T. Nagayama's *Taigai Shiryo Bijitsu Daikwan* op. cit.

[2] An account of this affair will be found on pp. 152–153 of Doeff's *Herinneringen*.
The mutineers were subsequently sent to Macau where they were tried and executed.

like his adopted father an official painter and art connoisseur. A contemporary document informs us that he was about forty years old in 1813, so he must have been born about 1773. The most flourishing period of his art was *c.* 1790–1830, judging from those of his paintings which have survived. The earliest of these is a large canvas in oils depicting a European hawking scene, in the collection of Mr. Morikawa. Both the subject and technique of this picture are purely European in style, and it has obviously been closely copied from a Western original of the late XVIIIth century, judging by the costume of the riders. Another and more famous oil painting of his, which appears to depict some Dutch colonial port (?Batavia?) with several equestrian and unmounted groups in the foreground, signed and dated Bunkwa 2 (1805), has often been reproduced [1]. A very similar and possibly companion picture in the collection of Mr. Ikenaga of Kobe, though unsigned is obviously by the same hand, as even a cursory scrutiny reveals, and can therefore be attributed to him with every confidence. Yet a third oil-painting of the same type, in the collection of Mr. Tanaka, is reproduced by Professor Kuroda in his book, but I have not seen this one myself.

Another oil-painting of a quite different sort, in the collection of General J. C. Pabst, though unsigned and undated has been attributed to Araki Jogen, by such eminent authorities as Professor Kuroda and Mr. Misumi, an attribution with which I agree after a personal comparison with two of the foregoing paintings. This painting depicts two XVIIth century Dutch merchantmen with a small hooker or shallop, and in general appearance bears more than a faint resemblance to the work of the Van de Veldes [2]. Of course Araki Jogen or whoever the artist was, did not necessarily copy some original Van de Velde; though he must have had either the original or a copy of some XVIIth century Dutch painting in front of him.

The above-mentioned four pictures are all in oils, and alike

[1] Cf. Plate 119 in T. Nagayama's *Taigai Shiryo Bijitsu Daikwan*, and the Album *Meiji Izen Yogwa Ruishu* for good reproductions. I have myself seen this picture at Kyoto, through the kindness of Professor Shimmura Idzuru.

[2] Unfortunately the picture has been somewhat over-restored. Like the other oil-paintings of Jogen, it is executed on canvas.

in both subject and technique bear strong evidence of direct European influence, but that Araki Jogen was also a painter of considerable merit in the ordinary native style may be seen by a perusal of Professor Kuroda's book. His skill in oils, which is much above that of most of his contemporaries, leads one to believe that be must have perfected his art by studying under some Hollander, and not merely relied on the rudiments he had acquired from his adopted father. The late Mr. T. Nagayama stated that Araki Jogen owed much of his skill to the instruction he had received from a physician at Deshima named Herman Feilke, who was an amateur painter of considerable merit. The truth of this is dependent on whether Feilke was in Japan before the date of Jogen's earliest dated picture, namely 1805; but it must, I think, be admitted that the latter did owe something to direct European tuition, whoever his teacher may have been. Araki Jogen was likewise a competent artist in the traditional manner. Some attractive woodcuts of his drawings will be found in the *Mezamashigusa,* a treatise on tobacco and smoking privately printed by Otsuki Gentaku (Bansui) in 1815.

Other exponents of the Araki and Ishizaki Schools. Chief amongst these were Araki Kuntan, Ishizaki Yusai, Doi Yurin and Kaburagi Baikei whom we will take in that order.

To the first-named is ascribed a very commonplace *kakemono* representing a Hollander with his Javanese slave in the conventional style, and which is alleged to be, on very slender grounds, a portrait of the *opperhoofd* Hendrik Doeff (1803–1817). Personally I see nothing in favour of this attribution, except that the individual represented is undoubtedly a man of the Napoleonic period, but whether the *opperhoofd* or one of the subordinate factors at Deshima it is difficult to say [1]. In any case both this portrait and the other works of Araki Kuntan reproduced in Professor Kuroda's book (Plates 26–30) do not give us a very exalted idea of his abilities as a draughtsman, though he was clearly happier with purely native sub-

[1] Kuroda *op. cit.* Plates 24 and 25. For other (and better) portraits of Doeff see that attributed to Kawahara Keiga and reproduced in the Albums of Mesrs. T. Nagami and Ikenega, and the one belonging to the present writer reproduced for the first time on Pl. XI of this work, and for an account of which see *infra.*

jects (*cf.* portrait of woman in the Ukiyoe style on Pl. 26) than with European.

The same observation would appear to be applicable to *Ishizaki Yusai*, the son and heir of Ishizaki Yushi, to judge from the sole work of his reproduced on Plate 31 of Professor Kuroda's book. Of greater ability apparently was *Doi Yurin* who is said to have died an early death at the age of 30 in Bunkwa 9 (1812), although the exact date is uncertain. A water-colour painting of Dutch and Chinese shipping (Kuroda, Plate 32), believed to date from about the Kwansei period or even earlier (*c.* 1790), is attributed to him; but a more certain and credible identification is the portrait in oils of a Hollander with his Javanese attendant (Plate 33 of the same book) which has considerable artistic merit and closely approximates to the style of Araki Jogen.

The fourth and last of the above-mentioned quartet, *Kaburagi Baikei* is responsible for the well known painting, still preserved in a temple at Shidzuoka, of the elephant imported into Nagasaki in Bunkwa 10 (1813), which formed the subject of so many contemporary paintings and prints by Japanese artists. This painting is accompanied by an explanatory inscription in Dutch, Chinese and Japanese, the lines in the former language being either written or dictated by Doeff himself [1].

The other followers of these schools need not detain us here, and we will pass on to a brief account of a more competent artist than any of them, namely

Wakasugi Isohachi. The works of this artist show clearly that he was entirely independent of the contemporary schools of Araki and Ishizaki with whose founders he was contemporaneous. As a painter in oils he ranks above either, judging from the three surviving examples of his work which have come down to us, brief descriptions of which are given below.

The best known of these three is an oil painting on paper mounted as a *kakemono*, depicting an equestrian hawker or falconer in the costume of *c.* 1750, riding at the foot of a curiously modern-looking sky-scraper poised on top of a

[1] Reproduced in Pl. 34 of Professor Kuroda's work. This elephant was the one sent by Raffles. Cf. E. Hahn, *Raffles of Singapore*, (London, 1948), 168–170.

steep embankment or hill[1]. The painting is signed in the right-hand bottom corner within an ornamented shield as follows, — *Nangasaky Wakasoegi: Jsofatsi Selfsafgeteekent en geschildert*, and if it were not for this inscription might easily pass as the work of a European.

The only other signed work by him, is an oil painting on canvas belonging to the Imamiya shrine at Kyoto, and depicting two XVIIth century Dutch men of war, of which one is apparently firing a salute [2]. This picture is likewise signed in Dutch by the artist in a bold cursive hand *Afgeteekend Door W. S. Jesofatie* in the lower left-hand margin. The name *Roojenburg* is decipherable on the stern of the right-hand ship, according to Professor Kuroda on whose book I have been compelled to rely, not having seen this painting myself. Although it is very well done, yet this picture does not come quite up to the standard of the other, and the execution of the waves in particular seems rather wooden and unnatural.

The third work attributed to Wakasugi Isohachi is an oil-painting on canvas in the collection of the writer, depicting mid-eighteenth century Dutch ships off the mouth of a river, which is unfortunately in too bad a condition for satisfactory reproduction [3]. Here again the technique and execution are so good that the work might easily pass for that of some eighteenth century European painter, and has in fact frequently been mistaken for such. The style of Wakasugi Isohachi is distinctly reminiscent of that of Araki Jogen, but the former is undoubtedly far superior in both technique and execution, and even if he was only a copyist of European works, he certainly copied them most admirably.

Nothing whatever is known of the antecendents, life, or death of this painter, except for the fact recorded by himself that he was a Nagasaki man. An inscription on the back of the *Roojenburg* painting dated Kwansei 3 (1791) refers to an of-

---

[1] Reproduced on Plates 35, 36, and p. 72 of Professor Kuroda's *Nagasaki-kei Yogwa*.

[2] See Plate 37 an pp. 75–7 of Professor Kuroda's work *op.cit.* This picture is usually referred to as a sea-fight, but since both vessels are flying Dutch flags and only one firing a broadside, I agree with Professor Kuroda that it is a salute rather than an action which is portrayed.

[3] This work is not actually signed but Professor Kuroda identifies it as being from the brush of Wakasugi, as indeed seems probable from a comparison with the other two.

ficial named Nakagawa. Professor Kuroda adduces some
reasons which would tend to identifiy this official with Nakagawa, Hida-no-kami, who was one of the *Bugyo* or magistrates of Nagasaki in 1795–6, and supposes that Isohachi may
have had some connection with him. Whether this was so or
not, the fact that he wrote his name in tolerable Dutch,
coupled with the excellence of his technique, makes it seem
probable that he had some facilities for visiting Deshima and
obtaining direct contacts with the Hollanders themselves.

Since Wakasugi Isohachi seems to have specialised in oils,
we may mention that there were other artists who worked in
this medium at the end of the XVIIIth century besides those
already mentioned in this essay. As nothing is known of
either them or their works save for a few stray references to
one or the other in contemporary records like Shiba Kokan's
Oranda Tsuhaku, we can pass on to a brief consideration of
the last and in many ways the greatest of the Nagasaki
painters who came under Western influence, and the only
one who as yet enjoys some renown outside the boundaries of
his native land.

Kawahara (or *Kawara*) *Keiga*. This artist who flourished
during the first half of the nineteenth century is chiefly celebrated through his connection with Von Siebold, for whose
monumental *Nippon* he drew many of the original designs,
especially those connected with the *Flora* and *Fauna Japonica*.
It is generally inferred that he owed much of his skill in
Western-style painting to Von Siebold's tuition ,but, though
he doubtlessly did owe something to the remarkable German,
there are several paintings from his brush which reveal strong
traces of European influence before Von Siebold's arrival in
Japan. Keiga's father is supposed to have been some relative
of Araki Genyu, so he might have had some lessons either
from Jogen or Ishizaki Yushi, of whose influence there are
indeed perceptible though not very obvious traces in some of
his works. Kawahara Keiga was involved in the so-called
'Siebold affair' of 1829, and his end is obscure, but his dis-
grace does not seem to have been permanent as there are
paintings by him from 1860 or later. He was a prolific artist
and many of his works have survived, (to say nothing of

numerous apochryphal attributions) so we shall confine ourselves to giving a very brief description of a few of his best
works which have some direct connection with the Hollanders.

1. *Portrait of the Opperhoofd Jan Cock Blomhoff and his
family.*

There are at least five contemporary versions of this portrait by Kawahara Keiga which all date from the same year
of 1818 or thereabouts, and differ only in a few details such
as the signature, state of preservation, and so forth. The first
and best of these was bought by the present writer in 1931,
but its purchase caused such an outcry in the Japanese Press,
with the usual "patriotic" repercussions against some of his
Japanese friends, that he decided to waive his claim in favour
of that of the Tokyo Imperial University where consequently
the picture now is. Although itself unsigned and undated it
bears Keiga's seal. A mere glance shows it to be the work of
a master, and no reproduction can adequately convey the
beauty and freshness of the colouring, although the figures
of the Europeans (as contrasted with that of the Javanese
which is superbly done) are a trifle wooden, and in places
relatively ill-proportioned. The picture is painted on silk and
has been exceptionally well preserved, the brilliant red of the
opperhoofd's coat retaining all of its original freshness. Although, as has been said, the actual painting is unsigned and
undated, inside the lid of its original box there is an inscription dated Bunsei 1 (1818) recording the circumstances
under which it was painted and the names and ages of those
depicted [1].

---

[1] A full account of this picture is given in Prof. T. Itazawa's article *Sakoku Jidai ni
okeru gaikoku fujin no nyukoku kinshi ni tsuite* in *Shigaku Zasshi.* Vol. 43, No. 1.,
January 1932. From a contemporary Japanese document, the names and ages of the
party (other than Blomhoff) were as follows, — *Vrouw Titia Cock Blomhoff (geboren
Bergsma) oud* 31 *jaaren; Zoontje Johannes Cock Blomhoff oud* 1 *jaar* 5 *maanden; Minne-
moer Petronelle Munts oud* 23 *jaaren; Meit Maraty oud* 33 *jaaren.* Another copy of this
picture is described by Anne Hallema in the January number of *Nederlandsch-Indië
Oud & Nieuw,* 1925. In the February 1926 number of the same magazine J. C.
Lamster reproduces and describes a screen by a hitherto unidentified Japanese artist
depicting Blomhoff and his wife with their Javanese servants. This portrait of Blomhoff is virtually identical with the portrait of him and his Javanese retainer (in oils on
silk) by Kawahara Keiga reproduced on plate 55 of the Ikenaga Catalogue; but in this
case the companion portrait of Mevrouw Blomhoff is replaced by that of the Chinese
'Captain' and his retainer. In 1937, another painting of the Blomhoff family was
recorded as being in the collection of Mr. Ito of Tokyo.

The second version of this picture which I have examined is that in the collection of Mr. Ikenaga of Kobe. It is essentially very similar to the foregoing, but is not in such good condition, and the colours are rather faded. By way of compensation however it is headed in Dutch (probably by some interpreter) *De opregte Aftekening van het Opperhoofd J. Cock Blomhoff, zijn Vrouw en Kind, die in A° 1818 al hier aangekomen zijn*. In the bottom right-hand corner is his *tsusho* or common name of *Toyosuke* preceded by the rather mysterious initials M E R (?) and written in Dutch as *Tojosky*, surmounted by a European top-hat inscribed with his family name in seal characters, which is reproduced in Professor Kuroda's work [1]. A third version of this picture exists somewhere in Kyushu as I was informed on reliable authority when in Japan, but as I have not seen it personally I can give no account of it. The other recorded examples have already been fully described by Dutch writers, P. H. v. d. Kemp, Anne Hallema and J. C. Lamster, in the pages of *Nederlandsch-Indië Oud & Nieuw* for 1918, 1925 and 1926. All readers will be familiar with the fact that Mevrouw Cock Blomhoff was not allowed to remain in Japan, but was sent back by the ship in which she came, as the Bakufu refused to allow white women in Deshima, except in times of grave peril, such as was the case with the refugees from Keelung in Formosa who had abandoned the place to Koxinga's forces and fled to Japan in 1661. Her arrival made a tremendous impression on the inhabitants of Nagasaki, and increasingly unflattering representations of the Blomhoff family continued to be produced by the painters and printers of the port for many years to come, a whole series of Nagasaki prints having been inspired by this theme.

2. *De groote Partij, in de kamer van het OpperHoofd zijn, op het Eijland.*

Of this picture likewise there are several copies known, all purporting to be by Kawahara Keiga. The best one I know is that in the collection of General J. C. Pabst, and has

---

[1] This painting is mounted as a *tsuitate* or small framed screen, a view of Nagasaki harbour by the same artist being painted on the reverse. For a reproduction of this last, see coloured plate no. 2 in Prof. Kuroda's *Nagasaki-kei Yogwa*, and Plate 53 in the Ikenaga Catalogue.

the artist's name and seal in the bottom right-hand corner. Though lacking the technical perfection of the 1818 portrait of the Blomhoff family, it is drawn with considerable spirit and obviously sketched from life. Professor Kuroda supposes the amorous *opperhoofd* embracing a rather coy geisha to be either Blomhoff or Van Sturler. If indeed it is Blomhoff, then it would appear he was not long in finding some consolation at being separated from his wife; but personally I cannot see any justification for this attribution, any more than for professor Kuroda's guess that the well-mannered young gentleman in the foreground talking to two interpreters is Von Siebold. The picture is undated and may possibly be earlier than the Blomhoff portrait. If this is so then the guilty *opperhoofd* is Hendrik Doeff, and this identification seems *prima facie* more likely than any other, since Doeff did have two children by a Japanese woman during his long sojourn in Nagasaki. In any case, the picture as a whole forms a very amusing group, with its many comical touches, such as the common sailor looking on in a quizzical way at the amorous *opperhoofd*'s advances; the man in the white suit and top hat settling down to some steady drinking quite oblivious of his surroundings; and the polite young man talking to the two interpreters in the foreground in a somewhat forlorn effort to raise the moral tone of the party, which if it continued as it had begun must have gone on into the "wee sma' hours".

In addition to General Pabst's copy, there is another in the possession of the Tokyo School of Fine Arts, which is the same as the former except for the omission of the Dutch legend at the bottom and its substitution by a Japanese title in the right-hand corner. The artist's signature and seal are also slightly rearranged. A third copy similar to that of the Tokyo Fine Arts School is in the collection of Professor Nakamura of Tokyo Imperial University, and I believe a fourth exists somewhere in Berlin. Incidentally, Kawahara Keiga was not the only Nagasaki painter who depicted these parties in Deshima, and quite a number of similar sketches by other local artists have survived, some of the gatherings represented being quite prim and proper, whilst at others the company seem to have been free and easy to say the least[1].

[1] Cf. reproductions in Prof. Kuroda's *Nagasaki-kei Yogwa*, Plates 47 and 50; the

We have no space to comment on all the other works of Kawahara Keiga, but apart from his zoological and botanical drawings for Von Siebold, the list of his paintings includes such subjects as Nagasaki harbour, Dutch and Chinese shipping, Dutch surgical operations such as blood-letting and so forth, and the Dutch factory at Deshima; reproductions of most of these will be found in the Japanese books quoted throughout this section. His portrait of the Russian admiral Putiatine and his staff, which served as the basis for the Yamatoya prints (in seven sheets) of this mission in 1853, has already been alluded to; but it appears that the artist was still working down to 1860 or even later, although this is the last signed and dated work of his which I know of.

Taguchi Rokoku, the son of Kawahara Keiga, who took his mother's family name, was also a Western-style painter of some note, though few of his works have survived. His favourite subject appears to have been Dutch and Chinese shipping, and his style bears some resemblance to that of Ishizaki Yushi. He was apparently involved with his father in the Siebold affair, but the date of his birth and death alike are unknown. Two fine paintings of his, depicting different aspects of Nagasaki harbour with Dutch and Chinese shipping are reproduced in Professor Kuroda's book (Plates 48 & 49).

Other Nagasaki artists. In addition to those mentioned in connection with the foregoing paintings, there were many other Nagasaki artists during the XVII, XVIIIth and early XIXth centuries in whose works European influence is discernible, but lack of space apart from want of trustworthy data forbids an enumeration of them all here.

Amongst the earliest we may mention *Matsui Genchu* who seems to have flourished about the Genroku period judging from his portrait of a Hollander which is reproduced in colours on Pl. 42 of Mr. Ikenaga's Catalogue. From about the

illustration on pp. 15–16 of the *Nagasaki Miyage*, (1847) and the earlier prints reproduced in *Hosaibankwa Dihokan*. These should not be confused with representations of the Hollanders at the licensed quarters in Maruyama which are fairly common. *De Groote Partij* picture is also reproduced in Prof. Kuroda's book.

same time may date the painting by an anonymous artist which is in the collection of the present writer. The subject is an *opperhoofd* with his Javanese slave, and in style and treatment it recalls both Mr. Ikenaga's painting and the early Hariya Nagasaki-e. There is a companion portrait of the Chinese "captain" and his wife.

Of a much later date is the interesting portrait of a *Hollander en slaaf* reproduced on Pl. XI, which is signed and dated *Getekent Door Toyokiti te Nangasakij in A° 1810*. There is some uncertainty about the writing of the date, which may be either 1810 or 1811, but in either case the *opperhoofd* represented must have been Doeff, who himself may have added the inscription *Hollander en slaaf* at the top. Toyokiti was in all probability the interpreter Araki Toyokichi, who was a contemporary of both Doeff and Cock Blomhoff, being one of the latter's helpers in his Dutch-Japanese abridgement of Weiland's Dictionary compiled about 1824 [1]. From his surname one might judge that he was some relative of Araki Jogen or his son, but this is only a surmise. The inscription and heading in Dutch certainly lend support to the view that he can be identified with the interpreter Araki Toyokichi.

Another artist of this period who deserves passing mention is *Matsui Kensan* whose portraits of a Dutch couple have often been reproduced (Kuroda, *op. cit.* Pl. 52–3; T. Nagami, *Nagasaki no Bijitsu shi*) and somewhat resemble Toyokichi's portrait of Doeff in style. *Isono Bunsai*, who flourished about the same time was the owner and founder of the colour-print publishing house of Bunkindo described in the previous chapter. He is the author of a series of paintings depicting Rezanov's embassy of 1804, which, although of no artistic merit, are of considerable historical value, containing a portrait of the celebrated circumnavigator Krusenstern who was then Rezanov's flag-captain. The influence of this portrait is easily discernible in some of the later prints published by Bunkindo and Yamatoya in connection with this embassy [2].

There were a number of other Nagasaki artists during the

---

[1] Cf. under no. 63 on p. 20 of D. L. Serrurier, *Bibliothèque Japonaise. Catalogue raisonné des livres et des manuscrits Japonais à ... Leyde*. (Leyden, 1896).

[2] The portrait of Krusenstern is reproduced in colour on Pl. III of Professor Kuroda's work, and a Bunkindo black and white print derived therefrom on p. 107 of the same book.

PLATE XI   P. 108

From the original formerly in the author's collection

Portrait of the *Opperhoofd*, Hendrik Doeff, by Araki Toyokichi in 1810-11

early XIXth century who took the Red-haired Barbarians as a subject for their skill, but the majority were so bad that they are not worth mentioning here. Some idea of their crudity can be gained from the typical examples of their work reproduced in Plates 60–77 of Professor Kuroda's *Nagasaki-kei Yogwa*; even a schoolboy might well be ashamed of such miserable daubs.

In concluding this section, we may observe that the different schools of painting which flourished in Nagasaki may be roughly classified as coming under one of three kinds; though the distinction between the three main types is by no means always a hard and fast one.

In the first place there are those artists whose art is mainly Japanese, and only seasoned with some degree of Western influence, whether in the subject chosen, or in technique and materials used. Typical examples of this type are afforded by Ishizaki Yushi, Araki Kuntan, and Taguchi Rokoku.

The second type were the painters in oils, pure and simple, whose leading representatives were Wakasugi Isohachi and Araki Jogen. They mostly copied European paintings, and attempted to follow European methods and technique as closely as possible.

The third and last category is represented *par excellence* by the master Kawahara Keiga, and has a good deal in common with the first-mentioned type, as native Japanese influence is still strong, though considerably modified by European ideas.

It should be added that this last-named class of painter included exponents of the so-called *doro-e* (literally *mud pictures*, so named because they were painted with muddy water-colour paints mixed with a large quantity of chalk) whose productions are almost uniformly crude and uninteresting. Another medium used by some Nagasaki artists was glass; but this painting in oils on glass seems to have been derived from the Chinese rather than from direct Dutch influence so we shall not deal with the question here.

Finally, we may say of these Nagasaki painters, that their influence was similar to that exercised by the colour-print artists (with whom they were in fact in some cases identical), though it was exercised on a smaller scale and neither so far reaching nor so profound. Still, they did their part in keeping alive that interest in and study of things European which is popularly believed to have become extinct in Japan during the Tokugawa period; and as such they deserve the gratitude and appreciation of posterity whatever their artistic short-comings may have been.

(b) *Artists of other schools*. Apart from the localised art of Nagasaki which was directly inspired by Deshima and its Red-haired occupants, the influence of European painting (especially in matters of technique) made itself felt in wider circles through the translation or perusal of books on art and the study of imported Western pictures [1]. The use of linear perspective in the Western fashion by some of the Yedo Ukiyoe artists has already been alluded to, and the influence of Western technique is further exemplified in different ways in the works of three famous scholars and painters in the later half of the XVIIIth century, namely Hiraga Gennai, Maruyama Okyo and Shiba Kokan.

Hiraga Gennai who lived 1723–1779, was a celebrated botanist and literateur who developed a taste for the study of Western sciences and paid several visits to Nagasaki to grati-fy his curiosity. He is believed to have learnt a little Dutch, though clearly his knowledge did not extend very far, and also to have studied oil-painting at Nagasaki, though who his teacher was is far from clear. The sole surviving work at-tributed to him, and one that has been reproduced *ad nau-seam* in Japan, is an indifferently executed portrait in oils of a European woman in XVIIIth century costume, which was recently acquired by the celebrated Kobe collector, Mr. Ike-naga, for a fabulous sum.

Maruyama Okyo, who lived from 1733 till 1795, has a greater and better-deserved reputation as a painter. Originally a follower of the conventional Kano school, he later on became interested in European art and was one of the earliest Japa-nese artists to adopt the correct use of perspective in his works. He also painted in oils (though where and from whom

---

[1] An example of this, is the Akita school which flourished in the Tohoku (N. E. Provinces of Japan) during the XVIIIth century, but Western influence on this school seems to have been limited to a few technical innovations, such as European methods of shading and perspective. Its origin is traced back to Hiraga Gennai.

he learnt this is uncertain) and some of his pictures in this medium have survived. One of his latest and at the same time one of his best works is a picture of Nagasaki harbour belonging to a Tokyo collector. The original is an elaborately coloured one on silk, being signed and dated Kwansei 4 (1792) only three years before the artist's death. A more enthusiastic and fervent admirer of European art than either Gennai or Okyo was Shiba Kokan, whose career is worth noting in rather more detail.

Shiba Kokan was born at Yedo in 1738, and originally studied the art of Ukiyoe under the celebrated Suzuki or Shizuki Harunobu. Becoming dissatisfied with this, he turned his attention to painting in the traditional *Nangwa*, or classical (Chinese) Southern School, with Soshiseki as his master; but although he attained to a considerable proficiency, as many of his surviving pictures in this style attest, his restless nature left him still unsatisfied and longing like the Athenians of old for some new thing. He tried his hand at making swords (*katana*), as also sword furniture such as *menuki* and *fuchi-kashira*, but soon lost interest in this art. When he was about thirty-six years old he met Hiraga Gennai, from whom he first acquired a taste for things European, which subsequent association with Otsuki Gentaku, Maeno Ryotaku, and other *Rangakusha* raised to a keen enthusiasm. It was copperplate engraving which first claimed his attention. The Hollanders had already imported several copper-plates into Japan about the middle of the XVIIIth century, but as no one understood the use or purpose of these materials they were returned to Deshima. About 1780 Shiba Kokan obtained (apparently from Isaac Titsingh), a copy of a Dutch work on copper-engraving by Bois (?Buys?),which he translated with the help of Otsuki Gentaku; and in 1783 he published the first copper-plate engraving produced in Japan since the time of the Jesuits and their mission-press in the last decade of the XVIth century.

Some of his later engravings of scientific interest have already been alluded to in previous sections (pp. 20–2, 55–6), but in addition to these he also produced a large number of sea-and landscapes, mostly copies from Western models and of rather indifferent merit. Nevertheless, his world map of 1792,

together with the astronomical and zoological engravings
which preceded it, constitute a work of real value and mark a
great step forward in the diffusion of Western knowledge in
Japan. Shiba Kokan's engravings are well-known, but he
had a less celebrated compatriot who also worked in this
metier, Aodo Denzen (1748–1822).

In addition to copper-plate engraving he took up the study
of painting in oils after the Western manner. His first interest
in this branch he probably owed to Hiraga Gennai, but one
account states that he wished to replace an oil painting in
Western style which had been painted by a Nagasaki interpreter named Tsuji, and lost in a fire at the Tenjin Temple at
Osaka. He went to Nagasaki in order to find painters in the
Western style but failed to do so, — a rather curious statement in view of the fact that there were several schools of
European painting flourishing in Nagasaki at the time. In this
predicament he was given a copy of Gerard de Lairesse's
Groot Schilderboek by the *opperhoofd* Isaac Titsingh, from
which he learnt the art of painting in oils. Shiba Kokan himself writes in his *Seiyo Gwadan* (1799) and *Oranda Tsuhaku*
(1805) that Titsingh gave him a copy of this work (*Schilder-
konst* as he calls it) on the occasion of his visit to Deshima.
Now so far as is known, Kokan visited Nagasaki or at any
rate Deshima for the first time in 1788, as we learn from the
account of his trip to Kyushu published some six years later.
Since Titsingh had left Japan for good and all in November
1784, he cannot possibly have given Kokan a copy of de Lairesse's book four years later, though he might of course have
sent him a copy through one of the interpreters or employees of
the factory. This is rendered the more probable by the fact
that Titsingh is quite likely to have met Kokan at Yedo on
one or other of his missions to the Shogun's court in 1780 and
1782. We know that Titsingh, when Governor of the Dutch
settlement at Chinsura in Bengal from 1785–1792, maintained a correspondence with his former friends and acquaintances in Japan, and it is therefore possible that knowing
Kokan's interest in European art he had promised to send him
a work on the subject after his return [1]. Another possible explanation is that Kokan did in fact pay a hitherto unrecorded

[1] Such is also the argument advanced by Professor I. Shimmura in section 9 of his

visit to Deshima in 1780 or at some time when Titsingh was there; but apparently all his biographers are agreed that his first visit to Nagasaki was in 1788, which would appear to rule this suggestion out; some indirect support for it can be obtained from the fact that various illustrations from de Lairesse's book are reproduced in the *Komo Zatsuwa* or *Red-haired Miscellany* published at Yedo in 1787, thus proving that the work was known in Japan before Kokan's visit to Nagasaki in the following year [1].

Be this as it may, Kokan translated de Lairesse's work with the help of some *Rangakusha*, and quite a number of oil paintings from his brush (besides an infinite number of apochryphal attributions) are known. Some of them are copies of European designs whilst others are taken from Japanese settings. All of them are painted after the European manner as regards technique. A good idea of his style can be gained from the pictures of his which are reproduced in the catalogues of the Ikenaga and Mody collections, and in the other Japanese works quoted throughout this section.

Although he continued painting in the classical Sino-Japanese manner till the end of his life, Kokan always had a pronounced predilection for the arts and sciences of the West, which he rated far above those of his own country. He wrote a small treatise defending and advocating European methods in art, — the *Seiyo Gwadan* published in 1799, — and scornfully termed Far Eastern painting a "children's game", reproaching it for its lack of realism and want of absolute faithfulness to nature. Although his work both as a painter in oils as in the conventional *Nangwa* style is still his chief claim to fame in Japan, he himself acknowledged his shortcomings in this respect, and always desired to be remembered rather for his geographical, astronomical, and scientific works which have been alluded to earlier in this essay.

interesting essay *Tenmei jidai no kaigai chishiki* (*Zoku Namban Koki*, Tokyo, 1925), and in his article *Yogwa Shidan* (*Namban Koki*, Tokyo, 1925, pp. 489–90).

[1] Another argument in favour if this theory, is that the careful and well-informed Dr. J. Feenstra Kuiper states on p. 294 of his *Japan en de Buitenwereld* that Kokan according to his own account (?where?) states he translated de Lairesse's book with the help of Gennai. As Gennai died in 1779, this, if correct, would mean that he must have acquired the book in that year at the earliest, as Titsingh only arrived at Nagasaki in August, 1779.

BOXER, Jan Compagnie   8

Apart from his activities as a protagonist and propagandist of European art and science, Shiba Kokan was a philosopher and political thinker of no ordinary calibre. Here again his ideas were strongly tinged with the notions of the contemporary European "century of reason", and some of his observations on Christianity, the closing of Japan, and other forbidden subjects must have scandalised the Bakufu. Curiously enough, outspoken as he was, he escaped the fate of Hayashi Shihei and many other advocates of Western intercourse who were far less zealous than he, and died peacefully in his bed at the ripe old age of eighty-one in 1818 [1].

The only work devoted exclusively to Western Art during the period in question is the above-mentioned little treatise of Shiba Kokan, i.e.

1. *Seiyo Gwadan* by Shiba Kokan. Published at Yedo in Kwansei 11 (1799) 1 vol. in-4to.

This work is now extremely rare. In addition to Kokan's statement about his getting de Lairesse's *Groot Schilderboek* from Isaac Titsingh, another interesting trace of direct Dutch influence is to be found at the end of the work, where underneath his name in Sino-Japanese characters is printed in *romaji* or European letters the word *Discipel* (*sic.*).

Although this is the only book which should strictly speaking find a place in this section, the two undermentioned works contain sections on European Art, and must of necessity be consulted by anybody interested in this line of research.

2. *Komo Zatsuwa* by Morishima Churyo. 5 vols. in-4to. Published at Yedo in Tenmei 7 (1787).

Partly derived from the *Komo-Dan* (*Oranda-banashi*) of Goto Ryoshun in 1765, the *Komo Zatsuwa* contains a good

---

[1] The best work on Shiba Kokan is Professor Muraoka's edition of his *Tenchi Ridan* (Tokyo, 1930) which contains a biographical sketch and an appreciation of his philosophical outlook. In this connection, Sir George Sansom observes (*Monumenta Nipponica*, Vol. I, pp. 317–319) that the views on art which Shiba Kokan expressed in his *Seiyo gwadan* were shared to some extent by Motoori Norinaga, the arch-apostle of the Shinto revival. Motoori, like Hirata Atsutane and many other Shinto nationalists, was bitterly anti-Chinese. Sansom adds that it is only fair to give the other view, as expressed by Kuwayama Gokushu, a connoisseur who, writing in 1790, said of certain realistic Chinese paintings that they were so bad that they might be mistaken for the work of Europeans. A true artist, he added, would never try to make faithful copies of things, for fear of being mistaken for a mere artisan.

deal of additional information, based on the experiences of the author's brother, Katsuragawa, and other friends such as Otsuki Gentaku, with the Hollanders at Nagasaki. A brief résumé in English of part of this book is printed on pp. 230–241 of the *Transactions of the Japan Society*, London, 1909, but no allusion is made therein to the sections on European art which are to be found in volume 4, and include reproductions of some of the illustrations and diagrams in de Lairesse's *Groot Schilderboek*.

  3. *Oranda Tsuhaku* by Shiba Kokan. 2 vols. in-4to. Published at Yedo in Bunkwa 2 (1805).

Like all original editions of Shiba Kokan's works, this is very rare. At the end of the first volume are two short chapters devoted to European-style painting and to copper-engraving respectively. It is in the first of these that Kokan alludes to Isaac Titsingh and the *Konst* (i.e. *Groot Schilderboek*) [1]. The second volume contains four crude but curious woodcuts imitating European prints of the Great Pyramid of Egypt and the Colossus of Rhodes.

---

[1] Gérard de Lairesse, *Groot schilderboek, waarin de Schilderkunst in al haar deelen grondig word onderweezen*, Various editions 1728–29, 1746, &c. Which edition Titsingh gave to Kokan it is of course impossible to say.

VI. IN OLD NAGASAKI.

The peculiar position of the Hollanders in Japan under the Tokugawa régime, as the sole representatives of European culture and commerce, resulted in their factory at Deshima becoming one of the most curious plots on the face of this planet for more than two hundred years. Naturally enough the unique position of Deshima and of its inhabitants aroused the interest and curiosity of both contemporary and posterior writers, whether European or Asiatic; and nearly every historical work published about Japan in the West devotes some space to a brief description thereof. Even the most superficial student of Japanese history is familiar with the excellent accounts of Kaempfer, Valentyn, and Von Siebold, to say nothing of those by other travellers or merchants such as Thunberg, Doeff, Fischer and Levyssohn, who have likewise left us detailed records of their mode of life in Nagasaki.

But whilst it is easy enough for the European reader to visualise from these books how the Hollanders lived at Deshima and the way in which they regarded Japan, it is by no means so easy for him to learn how the Japanese regarded their Red-haired Barbarian visitors and the impression these latter made on them. Practically nothing has been published in European books about the reactions of the ordinary Japanese "man in the street" to his glimpses of the Hollanders as he saw them disembark from their ships, or pass through the streets of the town on their way to the annual Shogunal audience at Yedo. Yet the Japanese have always been a curious and inquiring people, ever eager to learn about new things or strange ways, and it is obvious that there must have been some demand for literature dealing with the uncouth foreigners. That this interest did indeed exist is amply evidenced by the foregoing chapters which dealt with the prints, paintings and other artistic productions made to satisfy it; and the

From the original in the collection of General J. C. Pabst

Nagasaki *(Yamatoya)* colour-print of a Dutch ship entering the harbour, *circa* 1830

purpose of the present section is to give some notion of contemporary Japanese ideas about the Hollanders as gathered from the literature of the time, which it is both interesting and instructive to compare with early European impressions of Japan as recorded by Caron, Kaempfer, Thunberg, Titsingh, and so many others.

One word of caution must be uttered here. Whereas most of the European accounts we have cited were written by men of outstanding ability who all achieved unusual distinction in their own sphere of life, the Japanese records on which we rely were penned, for the most part, by quite humble merchants or petty officials whose daily business brought them into contact with the Westerners. But if in consequence they lack the keen scientific perception and critical acumen which distinguish the works of observers like Kaempfer, Titsingh or Von Siebold, they are none the less extremly interesting in their way, and of real value in revealing the qualities as well as the limitations of their countrymen.

The harbour of Nagasaki is one of the most beautiful in the world, but even its natural picturesqueness must often have been enhanced during the seventeenth and eighteenth centuries by the sight of the Dutch, Chinese and native Japanese shipping which frequented the haven. In particular, the colourful spectacle of some stately and gaily-beflagged Dutch East-Indiaman being towed to her berth off Deshima by a multitude of Japanese rowing boats, half obscured in the drifting smoke from the thunder of her saluting-guns, must have been one calculated strongly to appeal to the artistic sensibilities of the inhabitants of Nagasaki. That this was indeed the case, is clear from the most casual perusal of the paintings, colour-prints, and woodcuts reproduced in this essay and the works quoted therein, but this interest and appreciation did not stop there. Allied to a keen artistic perception the Japanese mind possesses a severely practical bent, which is forever wanting to know the why and wherefore of all new things, and loves to record facts with the most meticulous, not to say pettifogging detail. Several examples of this are to be found in contemporary Japanese works which make mention of the Dutch shipping in Nagasaki; and in order to give the European reader an insight into this type of literature we will give one or two typical translations in extract.

The first is from the pen of the celebrated Nishikawa Joken, the Nagasaki interpreter so frequently alluded to in this essay, and is a chapter of his *Kwai-tsusho-ko* (Considerations on the Chinese and Barbarian commercial intercourse) published by Umemura Yaeyemon and Furukawa Saburobu of Teramachi [Kyoto] in 1708.

"Red-Hair Ships

The average length of these ships is 25–26 *ken*, whilst the smaller ones are only about 20 *ken*. [1] Their depth is 7 or 8 *ken*, and beam 6–7 *ken*. They mount 22, 23, 24 or 25 guns as a rule, each measuring 8 or 9 *shaku*. There are four masts [2], each of which is made in two pieces, being joined at a circular top. These masts can be lengthened or shortened when and if required, whilst each mast is provided with two sails, all made of sail-cloth. Formerly ships measuring 33 *ken* in length sometimes came. The rudder is affixed .... [3]. The anchors are all made of iron, some of them being as long as 3 or 4 *ken*. The ropes are made of hemp, measuring 1 *shaku*, 2 or 3 *sun* in circumference. The black part of the hull is coated with pitch. The red-rust coloured part of the ship below the water-line is everywhere covered with small iron nails. These ships never require repairs during their lifetime. Their ship's gear, ropes, tackle &c. are all coated with pitch; pitch is a substance composed of pine resin mixed with oil."

Another brief statistical description of a Dutch East-Indiaman will be found in Rin(Hayashi) Shihei's explanatory inscription of his print of the *Schellach* published in 1782 (cf. Appendix II *infra*.). A more "popular" and at the same time perhaps a more typical one, is that written by a druggist named Ishida of Osaka, who compiled a valuable chronological summary of all the Dutch and Chinese ships which had visited Nagasaki since 1641, entitled *Tosen Ransen Nagasaki Nyusen Benran*. Although the author only compiled his work in

---

[1] 1 *ken* = 1.82 meters. 1 *shaku* = *c*. 1 foot or 30 *cm*. 1 *sun* = *c*. 1 inch or 3.03 *cm*.

[2] presumably including the bowsprit.

[3] the technical terms in this passage defeat me.

Tempo 13 (1842), yet much of it is based on older material, and therefore his account of Dutch shipping may well find a place here [1]. It is preceded by the description of a Chinese ship, which is likewise reproduced, since the Chinese were the inveterate rivals of the Hollanders at Nagasaki, and it is interesting to see how the Japanese compared the two.

"Concerning Chinese ships

As regards Chinese ships, when they have left Saho and arrived so near to Japan that they can be seen through the telescopes of the coast-guards on the hill-sides, information of this fact must be given as quickly as possible. Then, various officials and interpreters go out to the Chinese ships in small boats and exchange letters. After these formalities are over they return to the shore and the Chinese vessels come into the harbour. Generally the Chinese ships are very stoutly built and have three decks. The upper deck is constructed of planks so that even when it rains the interior remains dry and the water naturally flows overboard into the sea. The upper deck is the place from which the sails are worked, and where the ship's work in general is done. On the middle deck are the living quarters of the Chinese crew. The cabins are all fitted with locks and cannot be entered freely. The cargo is stowed below. In the centre of the ship is a deep cistern (rain-tub) from which water is drawn up by a bucket hooked on to a rope. After the cargoes have been unloaded, the Chinese ships are anchored off Umegasaki and all the Chinese go ashore into the Chinese factory. These ships have names such as [here follow various Chinese characters] and so forth . . . . . The primary quality of a ship is that it should be a speedy sailer, and for this reason they form the character [denoting "ship"] from "ship" and "bird". Furthermore they paint a large bird on the ship's stern for the purpose of avoiding shipwreck. Formerly the cargoes weighed more than 200,000 *kin*, but latterly on account of the decrease in the number of ships, they usually weigh about four or five hundred thousand *kin* (*sic*). I omit further details, only noting that the area of the Chinese factory covers 9,363 *tsubo*. [2]

[1] Cf. Ishida's preface translated in the bibliographical note at the end of this section.
[2] 1 *kin* = 132 lbs. adp. or 60 *kg*. 1 *Tsubo* = *c*. 4 sq. yards or 3.31 *sq.m*.

Concerning Dutch ships.

The Hollanders' ships on leaving Jacatra [= Batavia] usually take more than thirty days to reach Japan [1]. In the same way as with Chinese ships, on their being sighted by the telescopes of the coast-guards, the authorities are informed as quickly as possible. Shortly afterwards an official barge containing the *Kapitan* [so the Japanese termed the *opperhoofd*] together with various officials and interpreters puts out to the Dutch ship. Both vessels exchange signals with flags, and when this is over, the ship enters the harbour. The Dutch vessels are constructed of timber everywhere fastened together with iron nails, even in the most unnecessary places, the seams being caulked with pitch. They are so strongly built that they can even crash their way through ordinary rocks. The Hollanders possess a detailed knowledge of astronomy and geography so that they can freely navigate on the wide ocean and never miss their destination. The crews of their ships are ordered about and disciplined just like soldiers; everyone has his own rank and duties so that all commands are speedily and easily executed. On entering Nagasaki harbour, the ship fires a salute of guns so that it cannot be seen for the smoke; when this has cleared away, it is seen that all the sails which were formerly spread, have all of a sudden been furled. Likewise when the ship departs a salute is fired, and ere the smoke has cleared away all the sails have been set so quickly as to astonish the onlooker. Truly they can manoeuvre freely! Furthermore the masts cannot easily be lowered, so that even after they have cast anchor in port they always leave them standing. Likewise when it blows hard they can shorten or lengthen them if required, but we don't know how it is done. They never land the whole cargo at once, but change what they bring for what they export. Some of the crew stay on board the ship, whilst others disembark to the factory at Deshima. I omit further details only noting that the Red-hairs' factory covers an area of 3,969 *tsubo*." Ishida also adds a list of all the ranks of the various ship's officers,

[1] Incidentally it might be mentioned here that Thunberg states in his *Travels* (Vol. III, Chapt. I, p. 1 of the English edition of 1795) that the ships used for the Japan trade during the latter half of the XVIIIth century were specially selected and strongly built 3-deckers of the Kamer van Zeeland.

both Chinese and Dutch, which it is not necessary to reproduce here [1].

It will be seen that the worthy Osaka druggist rates the
Hollanders as better seamen, (by implication at least), than
the Chinese. Most Japanese writers agree with him, and Shiba
Kokan in particular in his *Gwato Seiyu Tan* of which more
anon, favourably contrasts the cleanliness of the Dutch vessels
with the dirt and filth often prevailing in the Chinese ships.

The foregoing extracts should give the reader a sufficiently
clear idea of the interest displayed by the Japanese in the
Hollanders' ships as such, and we will round off this section
by giving a typical anecdote from Nishikawa Joken's *Nagasaki Yawagusa* or *Twilight Tales of Nagasaki*, first printed in
1720. The incident in question relates to a fire which broke
out in the *Roode Hert* whilst anchored off Deshima in July
1665, a contemporary Dutch account of which will be found
in the Batavian *Dagh-Register* for that year. (*Dagh-Register van
Batavia*, 1665, p. 355).

*"Concerning the depredations committed by the Red-hair
ships at Fudasan, and outbreak of fire in a Red-hair ship.*

The Red-hairs were greatly infuriated at being driven out
of Taiwan by Kokusenya, and in consequence they thence-
forth considered China as an enemy [2].

Whenever they met with Chinese ships on the high seas
they took them, plundered the cargoes and killed the crews
in a piratical manner; therefore when the Chinese ships
bound for Nagasaki sighted the Red-hair ships, they behaved
like a mouse does when it sees a cat.

Thus although as a rule the Red-hairs were no match for
the Chinese in land warfare, yet in naval actions the Ce-
lestials could not compete with the Hollanders. Consequently the Red-hair vessels were strictly prohibited from visiting

[1] It is interesting to compare this Japanese account of the procedure followed on the
arrival of a Dutch ship at Nagasaki with the contemporary description given by the
Opperhoofd Meylan on pp. 351–357 of his *Geschiedkundig Overzigt van den Handel der
Europeezen op Japan.* (Ver. Bat. Gen. XIV Deel, Batavia, 1833).

[2] Kokusenya is of course Koxinga (*ie.* Kuo-hsing-yeh) who wrested Taiwan or
Formosa from the Dutch in 1661–2. The references to the Sino-Dutch war which
follow are interesting, but a clear distinction is not always drawn between the Manchu
Tartars who controlled all China save some of the coast districts of Fukien at this
time, and the Chinese followers of Koxinga.

the Chinese coasts, and on this account their attacks on Chinese shipping became fiercer and fiercer.

About the second or third year of Kwambun (1662–3), the Red-hair ships requested permission to trade at some place between Fukien and Ningpo, but were refused, and on the contrary the Chinese would not even pay for a few of the goods which were sold. This infuriated the Red-hairs, so they proceeded to Fudasan where they bombarded and destroyed a temple-pagoda, only returning after they had desecrated and plundered the Buddhist sacred religious furniture.

Now one of the ships which had taken part in this attack came to Nagasaki towards the end of the fifth month of the fourth year of Kwambun and year of the dragon (1665). It was said that they would unlade the cargo, etc. on the following day, but from about dawn some smoke was seen rising from the ship. At first it was thought to be merely smoke from a cooking-fire, but it gradually increased in volume until clouds of thick black smoke came pouring out of the ship's hold, and thus they finally realised that it was a serious conflagration. Now it happened that two of the guns were loaded, and people were very anxious lest these cannon should go off and demolish some of the houses in the town, more especially as they thought it certain that the south wind would fan the flames and consequently there was a general perplexity as to what ought to be done. The then Governor, Shimada, was also concerned, and thought that the ship should be removed to the mouth of the harbour far from the town. Accordingly on the orders of the interpreters, the Red-hairs hoisted sail and steered the ship, which was continuously belching forth flames from the hold, to a shallow place where it anchored. The Red-hairs speedily poured water down the muzzles of the two loaded guns and spiked them at the breech with iron nails, so that although they afterwards went off, they only did so very feebly. After the fire had got a considerable hold and had burnt the masts down, it was finally quenched by the great numbers of people who swarmed up and poured water down the hold. Although a good deal of the cargo was saved from the fire by water, yet the Red-hairs suffered a pretty heavy loss. Some people looked upon this as a just retribution by Kwannon (the Chinese Kwanyin, Goddess of Mercy) of Fudasan, but what the Red-hairs thought about it, I cannot say." [1]

In addition to the Hollanders' ships, the Red-haired Barbarians themselves, once they had landed, became objects of interest to the Japanese. We have several interesting accounts by native writers who visited Deshima (or the *Oranda Yashiki* as it was commonly termed by the Japanese), and its occupants. Since these accounts add nothing material to what we already know of the way in which the personnel of the factory lived, from the writings of Kaempfer, Von Siebold and others, there is no necessity to do more than to mention their existence.

Space must be found for mention of Shiba Kokan's representation of the *Opperhoofd*'s room at Deshima in his *Gwato-Seiyu-Tan* which is reproduced herewith (Plate XII). The original sketch was made in 1788, and not only affords us an amusing glimpse of Japanese ideas about Western furniture, but is of distinct value as showing us how Europeans furnished their houses in the East at that time.

Incidentally, whilst on the subject of Deshima, we may mention that the earliest known representation of this artificial fan-shaped islet in any map or plan, is on a map of Nagasaki drawn in 1635, in which year the site was actually reclaimed [2]. This map is of course manuscript, and the earliest *printed* representation that I know of is on a picture-roll of the sea and land routes from Yedo to Nagasaki published at Kyoto in 1672 [3]. The next oldest in point of time is the Empo (1673) map of Nagasaki and its harbour; but the earliest plan of Deshima in itself (as distinct from its forming part of a more general map) is the diagram at the end of the first

---

[1] What the Red-hairs thought about it can be seen from consulting the account of the incident given in Van Dam's *Beschryvinge van de O.I.C.* (ed. Stapel). II boek, Deel I, blz. 429, — "alleenlijck is het fluytschip 't *Roode Hert* soo als het voor het eylandt Deshima lagh, met zijn volle Bengaelse ladinge seer schielijck in den brant en voort weggeraeckt, sulcx dat de Compagnie daerby F. 124, 401 : 10 aen schade, buyten 't geene nog is geborgen, heeft geleden." (cf. also *D.R.B.* 1665, p. 355). Fudasan is the Japanese transliteration of The Chinese P'u To Shan, a famous Buddhist shrine and sanctuary in the Chusan Islands off the Chekiang coast, the sack of which by the Hollanders is briefly refered to in C. P. Fitzgerald's *China*, p. 482.

[2] Reproduced on p. xxviii of my edition of Caron and Schouten's *True Description of the Mighty Kingdoms of Japan and Siam*, (London, 1935).

[3] *True Description*, p. cxxiv.

volume of the *Nagasaki mushi-megane* printed at Osaka in
1704 [1]. During the eighteenth century these representations
became more frequent, the best-known (and most accurate)
being the 1779 bird's-eye colour print published by Toshimaya which has already been described in the print section of
this essay, and which served for Titsingh's *Illustrations of
Japan*. Of the innumerable representations published during
the early nineteenth century we need only mention the celebrated painting by Kawahara Keiga, of which at least three contemporary copies from his brush survive, and which has very
much in common with the plate in Levyssohn's *Bladen uit
Japan* [2].

To revert to Japanese pictures of the interior of Deshima,
indisputably the finest is the magnificent makimono or
picture-scroll painted on silk by Kano Shunko (1690) and
now in the possession of Prince Tokugawa of Mito [3]. In the
same style, and with only slight differences of detail, are the
makimono of Deshima painted by Watanabe Shuseki and
Hirowatari Koshu, two Nagasaki painters who flourished
during the seventeenth and eighteenth centuries [4].

The Hollanders used to visit Nagasaki occasionally even
during the time when it was still the centre of the Portuguese
trade with Japan, but it was only after their removal from
Hirado to Deshima in 1641 that they themselves became really familiar sights in the town.

All contemporary Japanese writers comment on their tall
stature, light hair and blue eyes, whilst their high noses also
came in for more than their fair share of notice, as had those
of their Lusitanian predecessors. A typical account of the

[1] The above refer of course only to Japanese representations of Deshima. An excellent view of the island was given by Montanus in his *Gezantschappen* (Amsterdam,
1669).

[2] There is a good reproduction of one of Kawahara Keiga's copies in Plate 33 of Nagayama's *Taigai Shiryo*, but there are many others on a smaller scale.

[3] A section of which is reproduced in colour as frontispiece of Paske-Smith,
Western Barbarians in Japan and Formosa (Kobe, 1933). There is another pair of very
fine makimono in the British Museum, portraying the Dutch and Chinese factories,
which obviously belongs to this school. Cf. also that reproduced in Mody's *Catalogue*,
Vol. II, Plate 160, ascribed to Araki Jogen.

[4] Two reproductions of a section of the former's makimono are given in Ikenaga's
Catalogue (Pl. 40) whilst that of Hirowatari Koshu is reproduced on Plate 34, nos. 1–11
in Mr. T. Nagayama's album *Taigai Shiryo*, whence four of the sections are reproduced and commented on in Dr. Feenstra Kuiper's *Japan en de Buitenwereld*.

PLATE XII

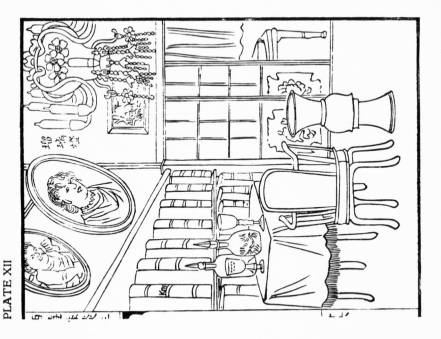

From the original in the author's collection

Shiba Kokan's wood-cut of the interior of the Opperhoofd's dwelling at Deshima, circa 1788

impression their physiognomy made will be found in Appendix I *infra*. Not only their persons, but also their clothing aroused much curiosity, as is evidenced by the publication in the *Komo Zatsuwa* (1787) of fourteen woodcuts depicting in the first place a fully dressed Hollander, and in sequence all his clothes including his undergarments. These are referred to by Japanese transcriptions of their Dutch names, and accompanied by brief explanations of their use and mode of putting on. In other contemporary works we find woodcuts of such mundane but essential European articles as knives, forks, spoons, chairs, tables, hats, gloves and so forth. In fact it can be said that perhaps the curious Japanese reader at the end of the eighteenth century was in a position to obtain more accurate notions of how the average European was clothed, than the European could of his Asiatic contemporary [1].

Nevertheless, thanks mainly to the distrustful and semi-hostile attitude of the Bakufu towards most forms of European civilization, the influence of the Hollanders on local dress, manners and customs at Nagasaki during their two century residence at Deshima, was distinctly less than that of the far briefer but more intense period of Portuguese intercourse from 1570–1639. For the most part only trivial innovations in local customs were introduced by the Hollanders, and the adoption, whether in whole or in part, of European dress for example, was confined to a few eccentrics or enthusiasts like Otsuki Gentaku, and these could only indulge their foible on special and private occasions.

Of strictly local influence in Nagasaki there are it is true a number of traces, but few of any importance. The Hollanders usually attended, frequently much against their will, the picturesque Suwa *matsuri* (festival) and the *O-Bon* or feast of the dead which were a feature of religious life of the town [2]. In one of the leading restaurants of Nagasaki

---

[1] This was not the case with political, economic or general descriptions of their respective countries, as thanks to the works of men like Caron and Kaempfer, Europeans were well-informed about these aspects of Japanese polity.

[2] An amusing instance of the way the average Hollander regarded these festivals is afforded by the *Opperhoofd*, Martinus Caesar's outburst in his Dagh-Register under the date of 27.x.1673. — A more cultured and enlightened attitude, in this as in so many other things, was that adopted by Isaac Titsingh who describes these festivals with the keenest pleasure, and gives a particularly effective account of the picturesque *O-Bon matsuri* in his *Illustrations of Japan* (pp. 143–4 of the English edition of 1822).

today there is still preserved a fine *byobu* or screen, representing the Dutch and Chinese onlookers at a Suwa festival of *circa* 1680. In the local industries of the place, the Hollanders, their ships and their personal effects (such as pipes, trumpets, and telescopes) frequently served as a *motif*, more often than not in familiar, comical or satirical vein. Dutch influence in *tsuba* or sword-guards has been dealt with by the present writer in an essay in the *Transactions* of the Japan Society, Vol. 28 (London, 1931). Other instances in different materials such as porcelain, glass and tortoiseshell (for the production of which Nagasaki was long famous) will be found in the Catalogue of Mr. Ikenaga's collection and in Vol. II of Mr. Mody's.

Some of the interpreters and other persons closely connected with the factory at Deshima evidently acquired a taste for European dishes and liquors, especially the latter, as is attested by numerous entries in the Deshima *Dagh-Registers*. The use of the Malay term *Makan* for cooks, which was at one time quite common in Nagasaki was probably derived from the Dutch, and translated old Dutch recipies are still preserved in some Nagasaki families. Titsingh's friend Narabayashi Jubei, whose possession of Dutch military books we have already recorded (p. 43), was evidently a man of culinary as well as martial tastes, if we may judge from the fact that his library included a copy of the 1772 Amsterdam edition of *De Volmaakte Hollandsche Keukenmeid*. An example of similar influence was the house of Narabayashi's contemporary and fellow-interpreter, Yoshio Kosaku, who had a room in his house furnished in Dutch style, complete with carpets, table and chairs, but such instances remained rare exceptions until after the middle of the nineteenth century.

The fact that the Hollanders were forbidden to bring their wives and families with them to Japan, coupled with the prohibition of any women other than prostitutes being allowed to visit the factory at Deshima, naturally resulted in close relations between them. On the whole these temporary unions seem to have been far from unpleasant to either party, and many of the most competent and dignified *Opperhoofden*, such as Caron, (who was not however actually at Nagasaki), Titsingh and Doeff were lavish in their praise of these frail charmers. Pictures of the Hollanders entertaining themselves with *geisha* are a favourite theme with Nagasaki artists; and in addition to those alluded to earlier in this essay, may be mentioned the woodcuts in the *Nagasaki Miyage* of 1847 and similar works. The scenes depicted are usually banquets either in the *Opperhoofd*'s room at Deshima or in the women's own place at the licensed quarter of Maruyama, whither it would appear the Hollanders were allowed to proceed freely, at any rate during later years.

On the whole it can be said that the relations of the Hollanders with the local inhabitants, as also with the local officials, became increasingly cordial as the years went by. At the time of their enforced removal from Hirado to Deshima in 1641, relations between the two races were embittered to say the least of it; and the contemporary *Dagh-Registers* bear eloquent witness to the numerous restrictions, vexations and humilations which were put upon the Dutchmen by those who were to all intents and purposes their jailers [1].

As the years rolled by, the Bakufu began to lose some of that fear which had originally been strongly tinged with its dislike of the Red-haired Barbarians. The loss of Formosa in 1661–2, though it had a most unfavourable effect on the prestige of the Hollanders in Japan, proved of some indirect advantage, since it undoubtedly lessened the fear the Japanese authorities entertained of their possible use (or abuse) of sea-power from their base in Taiwan. The visible decline of the Company during the eighteenth century, and the gradual spread of more liberal views in the Shogunate during the time of Yoshimune further contributed to improve mutual relations, despite perennial friction over commercial questions. The rise of the *Rangakusha* and the great increase of interest in matters connected with the West in general and science in particular during the last quarter of the eighteenth century, afforded a golden opportunity for the Hollanders to improve their position *vis-à-vis* the Japanese authorities; and it was unfortunate for the Company that none of the *Opperhoofden* then in Japan — with the single exception of Isaac Titsingh — were men of sufficient mental calibre to grasp the

---

[1] Cf. for instance the striking examples adduced by Valentyn in his *Beschryvinge van Japan* of the shameful way in which the Dutch were treated at Deshima during the first few decades of their sojourn there.

fleeting opportunity. The results achieved by Titsingh, and
still more the favourable impression and atmosphere he
created, prove what might have been achieved had his work
been followed up as it ought. Further allusion will be made to
this later, but it might be mentioned in extenuation that
the condition of the Company both in Asia and Europe was
critical in the extreme, whilst that of the motherland was
little better [1].

Still, the fact remains that the Hollanders at the end of the
eighteenth century were very much better treated than they
had been a hundred years previously whether in Nagasaki or
at Yedo. They were no longer required to sing, dance and play
monkey tricks for the amusement of the Shogun's concubines
as they had been on the occasion of the Shogunal audience in
Kaempfer's time. Titsingh, Doeff, and others of the later
Opperhoofden were treated on a footing of perfect equality
by many of the daimyo, whose ancestors would have had no
truck with any seventeenth century Netherlander. An excellent proof of the good social relations maintained between
Hollanders and Japanese in later years, was the way in which
Doeff was treated during the long years he spent in Nagasaki,
cut off from all intercourse with Europe, and with no apparent hope of relief in the future, when the Japanese authorities freely supplied him and his companions with money,
clothes and food without any question or hesitation. At the
same time it cannot be denied that this gradual improvement
in relations was partly due to self-interest. As the eighteenth
century wore on and the Company's trade with Japan gradually dwindled both in profit as in volume, so did the
private-trade and smuggling increase. Exactly the same is
true of the Japanese side, namely that the Bakufu bore the
loss, whilst Nagasaki and especially the Nagasaki Kaisho or
Chamber of Commerce (termed *Geldkamer* by the Dutch)
waxed fat and kicked. There is no doubt that the Nagasaki
Kaisho worked hand in glove with the Dutch skippers and

---

[1] Chinese commercial competition had likewise long proved a thorn in the side
of the Hollanders, even during their palmiest days at Nagasaki in the XVIIth century
after the expulsion of the Portuguese .... "The Portuguese having been kicked
out, the Chinese got much in our way in that fairwater, and they secured so much
of the trade there that we by no manner of means could make the profits which we
had confidently expected".

(too often) *opperhoofden* to the mutual profit of themselves and to the mutual loss of their employers [1].

Finally, a word should be said as to the comparative treatment of the Hollanders and Chinese by their Japanese hosts. Officially the former were far more highly considered. Their chief was given military rank and the status of a daimyo during his annual mission to Yedo, an honour to which the Chinese could never attain, though they more than once offered to bear the whole cost of this expensive mission if they would be allowed to undertake it also. In commercial matters, too, the authorities frequently interfered to see that the Netherlanders were not unduly oppressed by the concurrence of their more numerous commercial rivals, — just as earlier in the seventeenth century they had intervened energetically to prevent the victimisation of the Chinese by piratical Dutch attacks on their ships as reprisals for the loss of Formosa.

The attitude of the inhabitants at Nagasaki was not necessarily so favourable as that of the authorities, and a modern Japanese historian observes in this connection, — "despite the Shogunate's policy of favouring the Dutch merchants, the Japanese in general were not friendly with them, but entertained warm feeling for the Chinese simply because they were of the same race. Records tell us, that from January to December, in the 7th year of Kyoho, 20, 738 Chinese visited the brothels of Maruyama at Nagasaki, whilst the Dutch visitors numbered merely 270" [2].

This it not a very edifying way of comparing the relative popularity of the two races, but even if this standard of comparison is accepted, it does not prove as much as its

---

[1] For the Dutch side of this private trade cf. Feenstra Kuiper, *Japan en de Buitenwereld*, pp. 159–169; and Y. Takekoshi *The Economic aspects of the History of the Civilization of Japan*, II. pp. 160–181, for the Japanese side of the question.

[2] Takekoshi *op. cit.* II, p. 148. Incidentally a word of warning must be uttered here against placing too much reliance on this work, whose author's statements all require careful checking. The orginal work was written in Japanese, but whatever defects the vernacular edition contains, they have been multiplied a thousand-fold in the English (mis-) translation. Misprints such as Titing for Titsingh are comparatively innocuous, but when Danvers, the late XIXth century English historian of Portuguese India, appears as "a XVIth century Portuguese named Dunbar", even the most casual reader begins to wonder how far, if at all, Mr. Takekoshi has understood his original materials.

advocate imagines. For in the 7th year of Kyoho or 1722, only one Dutch ship visited Nagasaki — her consort having been wrecked on the way — as opposed to thirty-two Chinese junks, so naturally the number of Dutch sailors in the port can only have been about one-tenth of that of the Chinese mariners. Hence the devotees of Venus seem to have been equally numerous from either party. But apart from these invidious, not to say odious comparisons, there is nothing to prove that the inhabitants of Nagasaki were on less friendly terms with the Dutch than with the Chinese, considering the limited opportunities they had for real social intercourse with either of them.

In addition to the works of Nishikawa Joken, (*Kwai tsusho-ko, Nagasaki Yawagusa,* &c.) and Shiba Kokan, (*Oranda Tsuhaku* &c.), which have already been described elsewhere, the following may be mentioned as amongst the most important contemporary Japanese sources which deal in whole or in part with the Hollanders and their shipping in Nagasaki.

1. *Nagasaki Mushi-megane* by Jikoken Kanshu, 2 vols. in-12° oblong. Published at Osaka in Genroku 17 (1704).

This excessively rare little tract is the earliest publication exclusively devoted to the Dutch and Chinese trade at Nagasaki. It contains a diagram of Deshima at the end of the first volume.

2. *Komo Dan* (or *Oranda Banashi*) by Goto Ryoshun. 2 vols. in-8°. Published (n.p.) in Meiwa 2 (1765).

This exceedingly scarce little publication was the first book to be printed in Japan with reproductions of European letters (including Gothic type), since the publications of the Jesuit mission press at Nagasaki and Amakusa in 1592–1614. On p. 15 of the first volume is the picture of a Hollander, with that of his female counterpart on the *verso*. On pp. 29–32 are reproduced letters of the European alphabet in cursive, latin and gothic script. The reproduction of these letters aroused the wrath of the Bakufu, and the author was severely admonished, whilst all copies of his book were condemned to the flames. Hence the scarcity of copies at this present time. Volume II contains a woodcut of the *electria* or Leidsche flesch. The text consists of miscellaneous accounts of the Hollanders and the outside world as seen through the windows of Deshima, and served as the basis for the following better-known work

3. *Komo Zatsuwa* by Morishima Churyo. 5 vols. in-4to. Published at Yedo in Tenmei 7 (1787).

Reference to this book has already been made elsewhere, and a good idea of its contents can be obtained from the summaries given on pp. 279–280 of Feenstra Kuiper's *Japan en de Buitenwereld*, and Professor Honda's article in *Trans. Jap. Soc.* Vol. VIII, p. 233 ff. (London, 1909).

4. *Ransetsu Benwaku* by Otsuki Gentaku (Bansui) with a preface by Udagawa Genshin. 2 vols in small 4to. Published in Kwansei 11 (1799), by Koshimura Tonan. There may be an earlier edition dated 1788.

This work is a miscellany, apparently compiled by Arima Bunchu, a physician of Fukuchiyama, from Otsuki's dictation. It contains woodcuts and explanations of objects associated with the Hollanders, such as glassware, gin bottles, an ostrich, a cassowary, and world-maps. It is written in the form of question and answer.

5. *Bankoku Shinwa* by Morishima (Churyo). 5 vols. in 4to. Published at Yedo in Kwansei 1 (1789). Reprinted, Kwansei 12 (1800).

This compilation is more international in scope than the foregoing, and contains brief descriptions of the principal European and Asiatic countries in gazeteer form. Amongst the illustrations, some of which the author states he has taken from Valentyn's *Oud en Nieuw Oost-Indiën*, may be particularly cited the reproduction of a Moghul Indian miniature on pp. 16–17 of Vol. I; the double-page woodcut depicting the seizure of Pieter Nuyts in Casteel Zeelandia by Hamada Yahioye in 1628. (Vol. 5 pp. 21–2); and that of the Colossus of Rhodes, (which served as the prototype of several later Nagasaki colour-prints) on pp. 25–6 of the same volume. The first edition is distinctly rare, the reprint of 11 years later being rather more common.

6. *Oranda Sanbutsu Zuko* by Fujimoto Yoshi. 5 vols. in 4to. Published at Kyoto in Kwansei 10 (1798).

As some account of this work has been given previously (p. 52) no further description of it will be given here.

      7. *Nagasaki Bunken Roku* by Hirokawa Kai. 5 vols. in-4to. Published at Osaka and Kyoto in Kwansei 12 (1800).

This is one of the principal sources of information about Deshima and its occupants during the end of the XVIIIth and beginning of the XIXth centuries. Amongst the numerous woodcuts which illustrate the work, we may especially mention those of a fire engine and a Dutch ship at the end of Volume III.

      8. *Gwato Seiyu-Tan* by Shiba Kokan. 5 vols. in-4to. Published at Yedo in Kyowa 3 (1803).

Though not published until 1803, this work is an account in diary form of Kokan's trip from Yedo to Nagasaki and Hirado in 1788, and is illustrated with many attractive woodcuts by its author. Amongst those which are particularly interesting for our subject, may be cited the woodcuts of Deshima (Vol. III, pp. 11–12); a diving bell (p. 15); *Opperhoofd*'s room at Deshima (Pl. XII herewith); native sailors and coolies (pp. 16–17); Dutch ship unloading cargo (p. 17 v.-18), and the grave of Captain Duurkoop at Inahassa cemetry (pp. 22–3).

      9. *Oranda Tsuhaku* by Shiba Kokan. 2 vols. in-4to. Published at Yedo in Bunkwa 2 (1805).

This rare work, with its curious reproductions of European copper-plate engravings, has already been briefly described on pp. 115 of the present essay.

      10. *Nagasaki Nenreki Ryomen Kwan* by Uchihashi Chikuhon. One large unfolding sheet published at Nagasaki(?) in Bunsei 11 (1828).

This invaluable record gives a chronological list of all the Governors of Nagasaki from 1570–1829 (*sic*), together with the numbers of Dutch and Chinese ships entering the port annually from 1641 onwards, as well as a brief account of the principal events during this period.

      11. *Nagasaki Miyage* by Isono Harunobu (Bunsai). 1 vol. in-4to. Published at Nagasaki in Kokwa 4 (1847).

This interesting work, which so far as I know is the earliest book dealing with Nagasaki and its foreign commerce to be published in the town itself, should not be confused with the

PLATE XIII

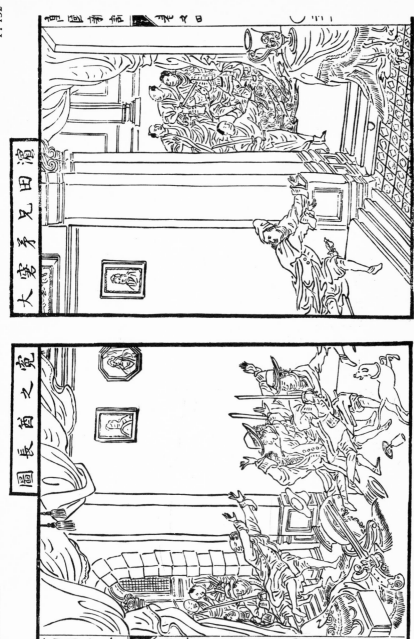

From the original in the author's collection

The seizure of Pieter Nuyts by Hamada Yahioye at Casteel Zeelandia, Formosa, in 1628, as depicted in Morishima Churyo's *Bankoku Shinwa*, 1789

work of the same name published nearly two hundred years earlier during the Empo era (1673–81); the latter deals only with the Chinese visitors and licensed quarters, for which reason it does not find a place in this bibliography [1].

Amongst the many interesting woodcuts in the text, we may specially note those of De Villeneuve's young bride (p. 16 *v*.); Hollanders and courtesans feasting at Deshima (p. 15–16 *v*.); and that of two Hollanders with a Javanese (p. 9–10). As noted elsewhere (p. 93) these woodcuts are from the hand of the Yamatoya master, Isono Bunsai.

12. *Tosen Ransen Nagasaki Nyusen Benran* by Ishida of Osaka. 1 vol. in-16° oblong. Published at Osaka in Kaei 7 (1854).

This excessively rare little work which was privately printed by its author, is invaluable for the history of Dutch and Chinese shipping in Nagasaki, giving as it does a numerical and chronological list of all Dutch and Chinese vessels which entered the port of Nagasaki between 1641 and 1854, together with some particulars concerning the cargoes, crews, &c. The compiler, who was a dealer in Chinese medicinal drugs at Osaka, explains his reasons for writing this treatise in a disarmingly naïve preface as follows.

"The particulars of the Chinese and Red-hair ships which come to Nagasaki every year were not fully recorded, — in some cases the date, in other cases the cargo or numbers of vessels being lacking. Furthermore the chronological system used was very complicated, and has become practically obsolete. Consequently, if anyone wished to investigate these matters, even if he gave himself a lot of trouble, he could not obtain any clear results. I cannot say why the people concerned with that trade did not clear the matter up, but I have been considering it for many years, in the course of which I have collected transcripts of a great many documents dealing with the subject. I have now reviewed all this material, and as a result have compiled this small volume called *Nyusen Benran*. However, as the old system of chronology is very compli-

---

[1] I was once offered a copy of this rare work by a Tokyo bookseller, but as the price asked was several hundred yen, and the book itself of no direct connection with European intercourse, I did not avail myself of this opportunity. Unfortunately I cannot remember the exact year or place of publication.

cated and beyond my poor ability to deal with accurately, there may be some mistakes in this work for which I ask the reader's pardon.

Tempo, 13th year (1842), spring. Respectfully written by Mr. Ishida of Naniwa (Osaka)."

The work is illustrated with three charming little woodcuts comprising (i) entry of a Dutch ship into the haven of Nagasaki at sunrise; (ii) Chinese religious procession in honour of Bosa (?); (iii) Dutch and Chinese ships; (reduced from those in the *Nagasaki Bunken Roku*). The Dutch ship in (iii) above, is reproduced as a vignette to the title-page of the present work.

VII. ISAAC TITSINGH, 1745–1812

Isaac Titsingh was the son of Albertus Titsingh and his second wife, Catharina Bitter. He must have been born at Amsterdam at the end of 1744, or early in the following year, judging from the fact that his baptism at the Amstelkerk in that city is recorded as having taken place on the 21st of January, 1745.

He came of a distinguished though hardly outstanding Amsterdam family, his grandfather, likewise called Isaac, having been a brother of the celebrated surgeon Abraham Titsingh (1684–1776), author of numerous surgical treatises which enjoyed a considerable reputation in their day. Other members of the family achieved similar distinction as sea-farers or surgeons, and it is not surprising therefore that Isaac was brought up in the first instance as a surgeon.

In March 1764 he was elected a freeman, but the turning point in his life came two years later when he embarked for Batavia in the service of the O.I.C. His early years in the Indies seem to have escaped the notice of all biographers, his first important post being that of Tweede Administrateur of the Graanmagazijn at Batavia in 1773. It may perhaps be mentioned in passing that the Graanmagazijn, used, as its name implies, for the storage of rice, wheat, biscuit, beans, pease and other foods, is one of the few surviving buildings of Old Batavia and changed but little since Titsingh's day [1].

It is to be presumed that he acquitted himself in this post to the satisfaction of his superiors, for in 1779 he was appointed to the responsible if onerous post of *Opperhoofd* of the Company's establishment in Japan. Before sketching

[1] The first posts of Titsingh in the government service and as an officer in the militia at Batavia, are briefly recorded in Wijnaendts van Resandt, *De Gezaghebbers der Oost-Indische Compagnie op hare buiten-comptoiren in Azie*, (Amsterdam, 1944), 173.

his activities there, it may be as well briefly to depict the
political and economic situation of that Empire at the time
of his arrival, in order to arrive at a just estimate of his
subsequent achievements.

Japan was at this time under the nominal rule of the tenth
Tokugawa Shogun, Ieharu, but the real power was exercised
by his two favourites, the minister Tanuma Mototsugu and
his son Tanuma Mototomo, Yamashiro-no-kami, the former
of whom was probably the best-hated man in Japan on account
of his corrupt and grasping rule.

It should also be mentioned that almost the whole country
— but especially the ill-starred Tohoku or North-Eastern
district, — was on the verge of an appalling famine which
held the nation in its grip from 1781 till 1788, and resulted in
a decrease in the population by nearly one and a quarter
million souls. In the first census taken after the famine was
over, the non-samurai population of Japan stood at 24,891,
441, — "the lowest figure recorded in any census of the
Tokugawa period, and a fitting culmination to an era noted
in the history of Japan as a time of starvation and misery" [1].
Nevertheless, despite these gloomy economic and social
conditions, this era was also one in which European influence
made a great advance, as is evident from the list of works
which were published during these troubled years by noted
Dutch scholars such as Otsuki Gentaku, Hayashi Shihei,
Katsuragawa Hoshu, and Shiba Kokan, to which allusion
was made in the previous chapter. Apart from this purely
intellectual current, some of the more liberal-minded people
began to entertain the idea of closer and wider political
and economic contact with the West, to which further reference will be made later on.

Having thus lightly sketched in the political and economic
background at the time of Titsingh's arrival at Deshima, it
remains to say a few words about the condition of the Hollanders in Japan, and the way in which they were treated
by the Japanese. It need hardly be said that between the
two races there was a great gulf fixed. In addition to the

---

[1] For the Tanuma regime and the great famine of Tenmei, see Murdoch, *History*,
III, pp. 379–84 & 394–405. The standard work on the period in Japanese is I. Toku-
tomi, *Kinsei Nihon Kokumin-shi*, Vol. 23 (*Tanuma-jidai*), Tokyo, 1936.

inevitable difference between an Oriental and an Occidental civilization, social conditions imposed another almost insurmountable obstacle to the attainment of a good understanding between Hollanders and Japanese. In Japan, which had been ruled by a military bureaucracy in one form or another since the year 1190, when Minamoto Yoritomo first established the Shogunate at Kamakura, the samurai or soldier was at the head of the rigid class system into which the population was divided, whilst the merchant and trader were the lowest in the scale, — at least in theory if not in practice. The official view of a merchant's status in Tokugawa Japan is perfectly emphasised in a letter written by the second Tokugawa Shogun, Hidetada, to the King of Siam in 1623, wherein the Japanese ruler exhorts the Siamese monarch to exterminate any Japanese merchants who might support his rebel Cambodian vassals, concluding with the drastic assertion that "merchants are fond of gain and given up to greed, and abominable fellows of this kind ought not to escape punishment." [1].

This overweening contempt for the mercantile class was in glaring contrast to the privileged position that merchants enjoyed in Holland, where an *Opperkoopman* was a far greater and more important personage than any military or naval captain. Still more was this the case with a great trading body like the V.O.C., which had a sharply graded social hierarchy with "heele Heeren" like the *Opperhoofden* or *Raaden van Indie* at the top of it, who usually had nothing but contempt for members of the military profession. The assertion that the status of a soldier or sailor in Batavia was little better than that of the despised soldiery in contemporary China may sound like a fantastic exaggeration, but the following instance is one of many which might be quoted to prove that it is not. [2])

When a detachment of the Navy under the command of Schout-bij-Nacht Van Braam was sent to the Indies from Holland on the conclusion of the fourth English War, this

[1] E. M. Satow, *Notes on the intercourse between Japan & Siam*, Trans. As. Soc. Jap. (1884), p. 160.

[2] J. C. de Jonge, *Geschiedenis van het Nederlandsche Zeewesen*. IV, p. 125. (Haarlem, 1861).

squadron put in at Batavia. The Rear-Admiral and his captains were entertained at a state dinner by the Governor-General, on which occasion Van Braam was disgusted to see an officer in full uniform, with a sword by his side, waiting bareheaded behind the Governor-General's chair like any humble domestic servant, — "a humiliation", he notes in his Journal, "for the whole officer corps, which is insupportable for any right-thinking officer and man of honour, and one which I cannot recall as happening anywhere else but at Batavia." The wonder is not, indeed, that there was such frequent friction and so many misunderstandings between the Bakufu and Jan Compagnie in Japan during the eighteenth century, but that their relations were no worse, and that on the whole they survived the strain with credit.

Despite the great difference in outlook which has been clearly brought out in the foregoing paragraphs, and despite the language difficulty, the intransigeance of Japanese petty officials, and — be it added — the lethargic incompetence of many of the Dutch *Opperhoofden* in Japan, there was a great improvement in the social position of the Hollanders, as distinct from their commercial dealings, during the eighteenth century. If we compare the accounts of the audiences at the Shogun's court during the seventeenth century as related in the works of Kaempfer, Valentijn, and Van Dam, with those given by Thunberg, Titsingh and Doeff a hundred years later, we find that the Japanese treatment of the Hollanders had improved out of all recognition. No longer were the Dutchmen required to play childish pranks or submit to humiliating mimicry for the amusement of the Shogun's concubines. On the contrary they were treated with esteem and respect. The *Opperhoofd* was given the rank and status of a daimyo during the annual mission to Court, since nobody outside the ranks of the higher military caste could be received in formal audience by the shogun.

The only irritation — if such it really was — which the Hollanders experienced on these occasions, was the curious throng who pressed about them in the antechambers of the Palace, requesting them to write something in European letters — usually an auspicious word like *Kraanvogel* or *Bamboe* — on their fans or on pieces of paper. This habit, which still persists in Japan, did not go beyond the bounds of friendly curiosity and can have given no real cause for complaint.

It has been mentioned elsewhere that the better treatment accorded to the Hollanders, as also the revived interest in western learning, dated from the time of the enlightened Yoshimune, who displayed considerable interest in western sciences and who — probably on the suggestions of Aoki Bunzo and Nishikawa Joken — even encouraged the importation and translation of Dutch books. Under these circumstances it is not surprising that the Dutch scholars, or at any rate such of them as had some official connection with the Red-haired Barbarians, began to visit the Hollanders in their inn, the *Nagasaki-ya* as it was called, during their brief sojourn on these occasions in Yedo.

It is a pity that the Company was on the whole so poorly served by its Deshima agents, who devoted all their energies to filling their pockets by private trade, with the connivance of the Nagasaki officials, rather than to advancing the interest of their nation and employers by seizing the opportunities offered them. Undeniably they had not a few difficulties to contend with; but on the whole one may agree with Professor Murdoch's sweeping if uncharitable judgement that "they took no interest in what was going on around them, and generally conducted themselves in a fashion that did little to win for them the respect of those Japanese who were really desirous of knowing something about the civilization of Holland. As a rule they had no interests beyond their ledgers, their guilders and their schnapps; and, being not incorrectly estimated by the Japanese as dollar grinders pure and simple, they were regarded by the best of them with a good deal of not undeserved contempt." The same illustrious authority cites the following anecdote in proof of his indictment. At Batavia, Thunberg tells us that Feith, with whom he had gone on the embassy to Yedo in 1776, on being asked at table what the name of the ruling Shogun was, had to confess that he did not know. Yet Feith had been in Japan fourteen years, and had headed the mission to the Shogun's Court no fewer than five times. The amount of intelligent interest which he took in his general surroundings was evidently not very great. [1]

It must also be admitted that even during the seventeenth century, when the average *Opperhoofden* were men of far greater ability than nonentities like Feith, they did not concern themselves much with the manners and customs of the people amongst whom their lot was temporarily cast. Thus Martinus Caesar, the *Opperhoofd* of Deshima in 1672-3, and a man of unquestioned ability, when taken to see the historic Suwa festival at Nagasaki, bitterly complained of having to watch "a lot of monkey play and juggling tricks, although we had plenty of other business to attend to." [2] Since this was undoubtedly the attitude of the average Hollander in Japan, or for that matter the state of mind of any ordinary European towards an Asiatic race, it is all the more to Titsingh's credit that he proved himself a much keener and more intelligent observer than his fellows. In this connection, and to anticipate matters slightly, the result of Titsingh's experiences in Japan is worth recording here.

In 1781, the Board of Directors in Holland wrote to the authorities at Batavia, asking them to ascertain why none of their employees at Deshima had ever tried to learn Japanese. The *Heeren Seventien* pointed out that many of the native interpreters spoke and wrote Dutch fluently, whilst the Tokugawa officials were anxious to be kept informed of political and cultural developments in Europe. The matter was later referred to Titsingh, who replied that the reason was not lack of opportunity but want of initiative on the Dutch side. He suggested that the Director of the Deshima post should be selected not merely for his commercial acu-

---

[1] Murdoch, *History*, III, p. 499. In fairness to Arend Willem Feith it should be pointed out that the personal name of the ruling Shogun was never mentioned in ordinary conversation in Japan, any more than that of a reigning Emperor is nowadays; so that this knowledge was not so easily acquired as the learned Professor implies. Furthermore, Hayashi Shihei and Shiba Kokan both refer to Feith appreciatively in their works, though it does not appear that his help to Japanese scholars consisted of anything more than giving or lending them European books. It must be admitted that Feith and his contemporaries cut a lamentable figure beside Titsingh.

[2] Deshima Dagh-Register, 27.X.1673. quoted in *Trans. As. Soc. Jap.* II Ser. Vol. VII, p. 166 n. Of course there were exceptions, amongst whom we need only mention two, François Caron and Johannes Camphuys, both of whom were keenly interested in things Japanese and showed an intelligent appreciation of Japanese civilization.

men, but with some regard to his educational attainments. The Japanese, he averred, were more impressed with academic or scientific rather than with mere business ability. Moreover, the Company would ultimately reap concrete commercial benefits from improved personal relations. The Batavian Councillors took due note of Titsingh's suggestion; but they added with disarming complacency, in their covering letter to the Directors, "that this is easier said than done, since it is a general rule in these parts to sacrifice to Mercury, but never to Pallas."

Having been selected for the responsible post of *Opperhoofd* in Japan in 1779, Titsingh sailed from Batavia on the 27th of June of that year, reaching Nagasaki on the 15th of August. Here he took over the factory from Arend Willem Feith under none too satisfactory conditions. Almost at once, however, he began to effect a change for the better. The steady fall in the value of Dutch exports from Japan and the constant quarrels of the Hollanders with the Japanese officials over commercial matters, had been uniformly ascribed by all preceding *Opperhoofden* as due to the corruption of the interpreters and rapacity of the Nagasaki Bugyo or Governors. Titsingh at once set about establishing friendlier relations, and his own comments about the interpreters are highly significant, especially when taken in conjunction with his above quoted remarks.

"Far from finding them suspicious and reluctant, as Europeans are usually pleased to represent these persons in order to palliate their own indolence, they manifested, on the contrary, an eagerness to procure for me every practicable information, to consult in various matters beyond their capacity the best informed individuals among the magistrates and clergy, and to furnish me with books which might serve as a guide to my labours."

Nor did Titsingh's efforts stop here, for through a student-interpreter he managed to get on excellent terms with one of the two Nagasaki Bugyo, namely Kuze, Tango-no-kami, a protégé of the Tanuma, who appears in Titsingh's official correspondence as "de braaf Gouverneur." The reasons for his speedy and astonishing success in dealing with the local Japanese officials are well expressed by Professor Murdoch who observes, "He kept profit-making in its proper place — which was the background — and promoted his advantage and that of his employers by displaying a real and unfeigned interest in the institutions, the sociology, and the history of the people among whom his lot was not unhappily cast for the time being." [1]

Titsingh left Nagasaki on his first visit to Yedo on the 19th of February 1780, reaching his destination on the 25th of March. He was received in audience by the Shogun Ieharu on the 5th of April, and after a farewell audience from the Roju or Great Council five days later, he left Yedo on the 14th of the same month for Nagasaki where he arrived on the 27th of May. [2] Short as his stay in Yedo thus was, he doubtless met on this occasion those Japanese nobles and scholars with whom he continued to correspond for the next two decades. Usually it was the physician of the Dutch mission who was the centre of attraction for the *Rangakusha*, and this natural inclination was probably strengthened by the impression made by Thunberg a few years before. It must therefore have been all the more surprising for the Japanese to find at the head of the embassy a man of extensive learning and rare mental ability. Naturally enough, with the real intellectual society of Yedo, Titsingh at once became exceedingly popular, and amongst his friends were Shimazu Shigehide, the *Inkyo* or retired daimyo of Satsuma, and Kuchiki Samon (Masatsuna) daimyo of Fukuchiyama in Tamba, with the last of whom Titsingh speedily became and remained on really intimate terms.

On the conclusion of his first year's tour in Japan, Titsingh left Deshima on the 6th of November, though owing to contrary winds the ship in which he was embarked did

---

[1] Murdoch, III. p. 503. Lest it be objected that Titsingh had exceptional opportunities, it may be pointed out that Kuze, Tango-no-kami, had been Bugyo of Nagasaki for five years previous to Titsingh's arrival, and both he and the friendly interpreter continued in office after Titsingh's final departure, when the Dutch trade relapsed into its former stagnant condition. The young interpreter died in 1787, of poison administered by his jealous colleagues, if the contemporary *Opperhoofd's* account is true. Cf. the document entitled *Aanleeren van de Japansche Taal door Nederlanders*, dated 26th August 1785, printed in J. A. Van der Chijs, *Nederlandsch-Indisch Plakaatboek* (1776–1787), Vol. X, pp. 803–4 (Batavia, 1892).

[2] All dates connected with Titsingh's visits to and residence in Japan during the years 1779–1784 are taken from his own records. (British Museum, *Add. Mss.*, 18100).

From the original in the collection of General J. C. Pabst

Nagasaki colour-print of an *Opperhoofd,* and his Javanese slave, *circa* 1780

not leave the bay of Nagasaki till the 29th, arriving at Batavia on Christmas Eve, 1780. The good use which he had made of his year's stay in Japan is evidenced by the third volume of the *Verhandelingen van het Bataviaasch Genootschap der Kunsten en Wetenschappen*, published at Batavia *in d'E: Compagnies Boekdrukkerij, By Egbert Heemen* in 1781. This volume contains four articles on Japanese subjects from the pen of Titsingh or from information supplied by him, viz.; A description *Van de Japansche Munten* (pp. 209–228); *Bereiding van de Sacki* (pp. 229–244); *Bereiding van de Soya* (pp. 245–6) and a list of *Eenige Japansche Woorden* (pp. 247–270). Only the second and third of these articles actually appear under Titsingh's name, the ubiquitous Radermacher, founder of the newly-born society, claiming vicarious credit for the other two; but Radermacher had never been in Japan and indeed confesses his indebtedness to Titsingh elsewhere. [1] None of these articles are of vital importance, but it is none the less interesting to note that Titsingh was thus responsible for the publication of the first detailed list of Japanese coins and the earliest Japanese-Dutch vocabulary.

So successful had Titsingh been as the head of the Japan trade, that he was reappointed for a second term as *Opperhoofd* in 1781. Leaving Batavia on the 30th June that year, he arrived at Nagasaki on the 12th of August. Early in the following year, he made his second *Hofreis* or journey to the Shogunal Court at Yedo, leaving Nagasaki on the 26th of February 1782, and reaching his destination on the 7th of April. His second stay at Yedo was also of comparatively brief duration, for after the usual Shogunal audience on the 13th of April, followed by the farewell audience of the Roju five days later, he left the capital on the 22nd of the same

---

[1] „Om hier toe te komen, verzocht ik de Heer Mr. Isaac Titsing, Opperkoopman en Opperhoofd van Japan, bij zijn vertrek in Juny 1779, zich nauwkeurig naar veele zaaken te informeeren, 't geen zijn Ed, bij zijne terugkomst op den 24 December 1780 met veel goedheid zoo veel hem de gelegenheid hadde toegelaten, bezorgde." (*Verhandelingen*, III. p. 205) Apparently Titsingh was not altogether satisfied with the way in which his article on the making of *saké* was printed, to judge from the following rather cryptic observation in a letter of his written from Amsterdam to William Marsden in 22. vi. 1807, — "as also the number of the volume of the transactions of the Batavia Society, with the year it had been printed, occuring sub nota(s) in the Fabuous History about Zakki". (British Museum. *Add. Mss.* 9390).

month on the return journey for Nagasaki, where he arrived on the 27th of May.

Owing to the outbreak of the fourth English war and its consequent untoward effects upon Dutch shipping in the East, the authorities at Batavia were unable to fit out any ships for Japan this year, and consequently Deshima re-remained without any communication with Java for the first time since 1719, when the three Japan-bound ships of that year had foundered in a typhoon off Formosa. Under these circumstances no relief came for Isaac Titsingh, who remained at his post as *Opperhoofd* of Deshima for another year, and made the utmost use of his enforced leisure by cultivating the society of his Japanese friends, and actively continuing his researches into all spheres of Japanese life and customs. Meanwhile he was far from forgetting the interest of his employers, and, despite the difficulties he had to contend with, he made use of the absence of the annual Dutch shipping, in order to extort from the Japanese an important concession in the long-debated matter of increasing the quantity of copper which the Hollanders were allowed to export [1].

This is not the place to record the commercial and political activities of Titsingh in Japan which are fully related elsewhere [2]; but it is interesting to note that when the ship *Trompenburg* finally arrived at Nagasaki with his relief in 1783, Titsingh permitted her boats to be manoeuvred in the harbour by Japanese sailors at the request of the local Bugyo, Kuze, Tango-no-kami. This unprecedented incident and similar ones connected therewith, such as Kuze's request for the dispatch of Dutch carpenters from Batavia in order to teach the Japanese shipwrights how to build vessels of greater burthen for the Osaka-Nagasaki coastal trade, were all straws showing which way the wind was beginning to blow at that time. There were in fact already

---

[1] For details see Meylan, *Geschiedkundig Overzigt*, pp. 211–220, and 299–300.

[2] Fullest of all is Meylan, *op. cit.* pp. 211–220, 223–234, 251, 292–3, 299–302, 309–11. See also Feenstra Kuiper, *Japan en de Buitenwereld*, pp. 145–50, 222–5, 275–7 and Murdoch, *History*, III, pp. 502–507. Incidentally, Dr. Feenstra Kuiper appears rather to underestimate the importance of the commercial concessions acquired by Titsingh, and I concur with the greater appreciation of his efforts shown by Murdoch and Meylan in their works.

at this stage a small number of men in Japan who were seriously prepared to consider the question of "widening the road"; and even if their views and influence were as yet strictly limited, still they appear to have had some support in the highest and most influential circles, to wit the Tanumas, father and son, who, corrupt as they may have been, were both undoubtedly men of ability and advanced political views. However, these schemes, whatever stage they may have reached, were rendered abortive by the assassination of the younger Tanuma in May, 1784, and by the fall of his father from power after the death of the Shogun Ieharu two years later, as Titsingh himself confesses [1].

After having thus stayed for over two years in Japan owing to the severance of communications with Java in 1782, Titsingh left Nagasaki for Batavia on the 6th of November, reaching his destination on the 12th of December, 1783. The government showed their appreciation of his successful conduct of affairs in Japan by the unprecedented step of appointing him as *Opperhoofd* for the year 1784, but with the express permission to return to Batavia after directing the trade for that year in Japan [2]. Accordingly Titsingh saïled for Japan for the third and last time on the 26th of June 1784, arriving at Nagasaki on the 18th of August in the *Trompenburg* after a very stormy passage. After superintending the sale of this year's cargoes, he embarked again on the 26th of November and left Japan for good at the end of the month, reaching Batavia on the 3rd of January 1785. Altogether, as a result of his sojourn in Japan on three separate occasions, Titsingh had resided in that country for a period of three years and eight months, and it is interesting to sum up the fruits of his residence from a cultural point of view.

In this connection, it is as well to hear what Titsingh

[1] *Illustrations of Japan*, p. 183. It would seem that Titsingh and the Japanese authorities had some discussion about the possibility of employing Japanese soldiers or sailors in the service of the Company, to judge by the following extract from the *Register op de Generale Resolution van het Kasteel Batavia*, dated 16.IV.1784, — "De Opperhoofden moeten het project om de Japanders in den dienst van de Compagnie te engageeren bij gelegenheid eens nader met omzigtigheid ten tapijte brengen."

[2] ,,Aan het naar Japan vertrekkende opperhoofd Titsingh gepermitteerd na het aflopen van den handel weder terug te mogen keeren, & om bij zijne aankomst aldaar immediaat het bestier over te neemen." (*Ibidem*).

himself thought of those Japanese with whom he came into close social contact. That he had a high opinion of their intellectual abilities is clear from the following quotation from his posthumous *Illustrations of Japan*; incidentally, this extract also serves to show that the knowledge and study of Dutch at this period had a far wider circulation than is generally realised, —

"During my residence in Japan, several persons of quality at Yedo, Kyoto, and Osaka, applied themselves assiduously to the acquisition of the Dutch language, and the reading of our books. The Prince of Satsuma [Shimazu Shigehide], father-in-law of the present Shogun [Ienari], used our alphabet in his letters to express what he wished a third person not to understand. The surprising progress made by the Prince of Tamba, by Katsuragawa Hoshu, physician to the Shogun, and Nakagawa, physician to the Prince of Wakasa, and several others enabled them to express themselves more clearly than many Portuguese born and bred among us in Batavia. Considering the short period of our residence in Yedo, [about three weeks], such proficiency cannot but excite astonishment and admiration. The privilege of corresponding with the Japanese above-mentioned and of sending them back their answers corrected, without the letters being opened by the Government, allowed through the special favour of the worthy Governor, Tango-no-kami, facilitated to them the learning of Dutch."

It is interesting to note that Titsingh's high opinion of his Japanese friends and collaborators was reciprocated by them. One of the Nagasaki interpreters, Imamura Kinbei, who is mentioned by Titsingh in his work, refers in eulogistic terms to the latter's earnest study of things Japanese in general and of social customs in particular [1]. Other contemporary Japanese records mention the fact that Titsingh's liking for things Japanese extended to his furnishing the *Opperhoofd*'s room at Deshima in native style, — a trait which recalls his illustrious predecessor of the XVIIth

---

[1] This information and most of what follows is derived from Professor I. Shimmura's instructive essay on *Tenmei Jidai no Kaigai Chishiki* (Knowledge of the outer world in Japan during the Tenmei period) printed in the *Shigaku Zasshi* of 1915–16, and reprinted ten years later in his *Zoku-Namban Koki*, (pp. 43–106). Nearly half of this valuable essay is devoted to Titsingh and his Japanese studies.

century, François Caron. His knowledge of Sino-Japanese characters and zealous study of the written language is also alluded to by some Japanese scholars who knew him. His connection with Kuchiki Samon's *Seiyo Sembu* has been mentioned elsewhere (page 20), but although the publication of this book was certainly influenced by him, his name does not actually appear therein. This is not the case with Morishima Churyo's *Komo Zatsuwa* (1787), or Shiba Kokan's *Seiyo Gwadan* (1799) and *Oranda Tsuhaku* (1805), in all of which his name appears and his help is specifically acknowledged. Why Kuchiki Samon, with whom he was on more intimate terms than anyone else, did not mention his name can only be guessed; but it seems probable that insular conservatism was still too strong in Government circles to make it advisable for a feudal lord to admit being on such familiar terms with a Red-haired Barbarian. Titsingh's close connection with Narabayashi Jubei, Katsuragawa Hoshu, Nakagawa Junan and other *Rangakusha* is also evident from the contemporary Japanese records cited by Professor Shimmura, as well as from allusions in Titsingh's own works; but the most interesting side of this connection is best brought out by the correspondence between these worthies and Titsingh when Governor of Bengal, which we will now pause to consider.

In July 1784, the Governor-General at Batavia and his council had resolved to re-establish the Dutch trade in Bengal, where the factory at Chinsura (Hughli) had fallen into the hands of the English during the late war. Under the circumstances it was essential to appoint a really capable man to direct the trade at this place, which had formerly been one of the most prosperous *buiten-kantoren*; and in the same year that Titsingh returned from his last voyage to Japan he was nominated for this responsible post, receiving likewise the rank of *Raad-Extraordinaris van Indië*.

Fortunately we are fairly well informed about Titsingh's seven years tenure of the Governorship of Chinsura, and the correspondence he maintained thence with his friends in Japan. In the first place, we have the narrative of the French traveller, Grandpré, who visited Titsingh at Chinsura in the course of a tour through Bengal in 1789, and who obtained from him an interesting account of Japan which was edited by Charpentier-Cossigny at Paris ten years later [1].

Secondly, there is Titsingh's own letterbook containing copies of several hundred letters written by him to various correspondents in Holland, England, Java, and China between 1790 and 1797, and which contains frequent allusions to his Japanese researches [2]. Last but by no means least, there is a collection of forty-seven autograph letters dated between 1785 and 1790, written to Titsingh by various foreign correspondents, including thirteen Japanese acquaintances. Whereas the first-named codex is preserved in the British Museum, the second has, appropriately enough, found a final resting-place in the library of the Imperial University at Kyoto in Japan. The following brief analysis of its contents is based on Professor Shimmura's remarks thereon in his essay *Tenmei Jidai no Kaigai Chishiki* [3].

Of the thirteen Japanese correspondents whose letters are preserved in the Codex, two, in the persons of Kuchiki Samon and Nakagawa Junan, were Yedo *Rangakusha*, whilst the remaining eleven persons were all Nagasaki interpreters, including Narabayashi Jubei, Motogi Enoshin, Imamura Kinsaburo and five others. The importance of this correspondence from an historical point of view can scarcely be exaggerated. Alike in its scope and duration it was quite unprecedented, and marks the first breach in the hitherto impenetrable wall of the *Sakoku* (closed country) or seclusion policy adopted by the Tokugawa Shogunate. It is also interesting from a social point of view. For the first time since

[1] An excellent account of Titsingh's political and commercial activities at Chinsura will be found in Professor Holden Furber's *John Company at work. A study of European expansion in India in the late eighteenth century* (Harvard University Press, 1948). The cultural and social aspects of Titsingh's sojourn in India are discussed in my essay, *The Mandarin at Chinsura; Isaac Titsingh in Bengal, 1785–1792*, (Kon. Ver. Indisch Instituut, Amsterdam, 1949), where a full bibliography of the relevant sources will be found.

[2] British Museum, *Add. Mss.* 18101. This is the first item listed in the Catalogue of Titsingh's library, printed on pp. 313–325 of his posthumous *Illustrations of Japan*. (London, 1822). It was subsequently acquired by Klaproth and passed after his death to the British Museum.

[3] This is the second item listed in the Catalogue of Titsingh's library (*op. cit.* p. 313). It was acquired in Germany by Kyoto University just before the outbreak of the war of 1914–1918, according to Professor Shimmura. (*Zoku Namban Koki*, p. 101).

the flourishing days of Jesuit influence in Japan, Japanese officials and men of rank corresponded with a European on equal terms, and on matters unconnected with political or official business. Such a proceeding was in direct defiance of the exclusion laws, and there can be little doubt but that its existence was known to the highest authorities, since one of Titsingh's most assiduous correspondents was Shimazu Shigehide, father-in-law of the Shogun Ienari then in his minority, and who by virtue of his relationship with the Shogun exercised exceptional influence on the direction of affairs. This again implies that the liberal party had by no means lost all heart on the death of the younger Tanuma in 1784, and proves the existence of a powerful, if as yet narrow, circle of influential intellectuals who were clearly started on the road which led to the open door policy of the Meiji period.

Amongst the twenty-two letters contributed by his Japanese correspondents in this codex, the most interesting are the five written by Kuchiki Samon, daimyo of Fukuchiyama in Tamba. One of these, dated Kwansei 1 (1789) third month, minth day, is particularly interesting as it contains the answers of Kuchiki to a sort of questionnaire previously sent him by Titsingh. The twelve questions asked by the latter, range over such varied matters as the origin of the Japanese race; the first arrival of the Chinese; the origin of Sino-Japanese characters, and the derivation of the *kana* syllabary; details of the Ebisu [Ainu] and Ryukyu characters; date of the burial of the last Shogun [Ieharu], name of the one then reigning [Ienari], as also that of his consort and so forth. Kuchiki Samon in an earlier letter (May, 1785), asks Titsingh to send him some geographical works, promising for his part, to send secretly some old Japanese gold and silver coins for which the Dutchman had asked. The Tamba daimyo also asked Titsingh to return to him his original letter, with the Dutch spelling and grammar duly corrected where necessary.

Such was Titsingh's zeal and enthusiasm for his Japanese studies, that he not only brought with him from Batavia to Bengal a vast collection of Japanese books, manuscripts, and coins, but also two Chinese clerks to help him in translating

classical Japanese and Chinese works. He was disappointed
in this last-mentioned aim, as both these men seem to have
died soon after their arrival. Titsingh's subsequent efforts to
get wood or metal matrices for Sino-Japanese characters made
in Bengal and Java likewise proved abortive. The English
at Calcutta, with whom he was on excellent terms, offered
him two *lacks* of Rupees (about £ 20,000) for his Japanese
collection, according to Grandpré, but he patriotically refused this generous offer. He hoped to get his works published
in Holland through the intermediary of his brother, to whom
he sent his manuscripts as he successively finished them,
taking care to always retain at least one fair copy for future reference.

Two of Titsingh's most intimate English friends had been
members of Dr. Johnson's immortal coterie, — "The Club".
These were Sir William Jones, the celebrated lawyer and
Orientalist, and Sir Robert Chambers, Vinerian Professor
of Law at Oxford, Puisne Judge of the Bengal High Court,
and Chief Justice since 1791. Jones and Titsingh had a
great bond in their mutual interest in the civilization and
history of Oriental peoples, something exceptional amongst
their European contemporaries; but whereas Titsingh con-
centrated his researches on things Japanese, Jones ranged far
and wide over Asia, if not always very deep. They dined and
wined each other when occasion offered, and exchanged
Oriental books and manuscripts on loan. These latter
included an old manuscript Latin and Chinese dictionary
of Portuguese Jesuit origin, which Titsingh assiduously
copied, "sitting as if chained to my desk", until it was
finished. An amusing sidelight on this friendship can be
seen in a letter written by Sir William Jones to his colleague,
Mr. Justice Hyde, in October 1789.

"When I express the hope of seeing you in two or three
days it is only a hope; for I shall affront the Mandarin at
Chinsura, if I do not make my annual visit to him; now I can
only visit him at night, and the wind and tide may delay me
as they did last year .... I have written four papers for our
expiring Society, on very curious subjects, and have prepared
materials for a discourse on the Chinese. The Society is a
puny, rickety child,and must be fed with pap; nor shall it

die by my fault; but die it must, for I cannot alone support it. In my youthful days, I was always ready to join in a dance or a concert, but I could never bring myself to dance a solitary hornpipe, or to play a solo. When I see Titsingh (who, by the way, will never write anything for us, as long as his own Batavian Society subsists), I will procure full information concerning the pincushion rice, and will report it to you."

The Society so disparagingly referred to by its founder was the Asiatic Society of Bengal, of which Titsingh was likewise a foundation member. Sir William's fears for its future fortunately proved unfounded. On the contrary, it was the Batavian Society of Arts and Sciencies which soon lapsed into a state of suspended animation, from which it was only rescued by the enthusiasm and energy of Raffles during the British occupation of Java. In his *Discourse on the Chinese*, delivered to the Bengal Society in 1790, Jones alludes in the most flattering terms to Titsingh's researches in Japan, comparing him to Kaempfer. He states that Titsingh intended to learn Chinese after his return to Java, so that he would be able to use the precious collection of books in Sinico-Japanese which he had brought back from Deshima. In this speech to the Asiatic Society at Calcutta, Jones anticipates in several ways Raffles' lecture on Japan addressed to the sister Batavian Society twenty-five years later. Both allude to Japan as the "imperial island", claiming for Dai Nippon "a pre-eminence among Eastern Kingdoms analogous to that of Britain among the nations of the West." Raffles, on the authority of his drunken Scots friend, Dr. Ainslie, repeats in very similar terms Sir William Jones' prior attestation (on the authority of Titsingh) that "the Japanese would resent, as an insult to their dignity, the bare suggestion of their descent from the Chinese, whom they surpass in several of the mechanical arts, and, what is of greater consequence, in military spirit" [1].

---

[1] Cf. the following passage in Raffles' speech to the Batavian Society, 10 September, 1815, — "Nothing indeed is so offensive to the feelings of a Japanese as to be compared in any one respect with the Chinese, and on the only occasion on which Dr. Ainslie saw the habitual politeness of a Japanese ever surprised into a burst of passion was, when, upon a similitude of the two nations being unguardedly asserted, the latter laid his hand upon his sword!" For further details see E. Hahn, *Raffles of Singapore* (London, 1948) pp. 162–172.

Titsingh corresponded with French as well as with English savants. One of the former, the Academecian and Sinologue Joseph de Guignes, informed him that the Bibliothèque du Roi at Paris possessed only one Japanese book, and that a very defective copy. Titsingh therefore sent this library a set of the *Dai Nihon-shi*, the monumental history of Japan published under the auspicies of the Tokugawa princes of Mito, in 243 volumes between 1697 and 1715. Owing to the difficulty of printing the Sino-Japanese characters in his intended publications, he considered the possibility of having his works printed in France or Holland, with spaces left for the insertion of these characters, which would be done later under his personal supervision at Batavia. Unfortunately, this and other schemes came to naught; and none of the Japanese material which kept him so busy in Bengal was published until after his death in February 1812, with the exception of some bowdlerized passages inserted by de Guignes in the *Journal Encyclopedia* for February 1789, whence the English translation in the *Literary Magazine* for March of the same year.

Although Titsingh in his letters to his family often complained of overwork, both in connection with his commercial duties as with his own passion for Far Eastern research, his life was by no means the unrelieved round of toil which the reader of his private correspondence might well imagine it to be. We catch a glimpse of another side of his character in William Hickey's inimitable *Memoirs*. From these we learn that the Dutch Governor of Chinsura "literally could drink gin like water," and this testimony, coming as it does from such a champion of the bottle, is convincing in itself, apart from the anecdote which Hickey relates in proof of it. The bibulous Bengal attorney acted as host on more than one occasion to Titsingh and his compatriots at Chinsura, where Hickey had a country house. He records of these convivial parties, "as I treated my guests with all the luxuries that money could procure, and the Mynheers did complete justice to the champagne and burgundy I gave them, my disbursements were consequently very large." Titsingh was not backward in returning hospitality to his English friends, and his parties were evidently more enjoyable than those of his predecessor, J. M. Ross, whose dinners were dismissed by Philip Francis as "plenty of victuals and civility, but as dull as Rotterdam." The pleasures of Bacchus were not Titsingh's only diversion, for whilst in Bengal he fathered a natural son, whose birth he kept secret from his family for some time, only acknowledging his existence after his return to Batavia [1].

Titsingh's efforts to revive the decaying Dutch trade in Bengal have been fully and competently dealt with by Professor Holden Furber, and the interested reader is referred to this authority for further details [2]. Although, as Professor Furber points out, Titsingh was neither so fortunate nor so unscrupulous as Ross, he managed to acquire a fortune of over 225,000 rupees in Bengal. His personal friendship with Lord Cornwallis proved valuable in more senses than one, though here again it was not so gainful as Ross' friendship with Warren Hastings, for these last two were almost if not quite as thick as thieves. Even Titsingh's forcible seizure of the English smuggler *Atonetta* off Serampore in March 1789, did not disturb the even tenour of Anglo-Dutch relations in Bengal, — partly, perhaps, because the Dutch Governor and his Council took care to send to Calcutta all the items in the cargo which were shipped as gifts to prominent residents. It was apparently in this year that the Dutch settlement at Baranagore was exchanged with the English for some land nearer Hughli and Chinsura, in accordance with Titsingh's own suggestion. The Dutch Governor had his difficulties with the English over the lucrative opium contracts and other sources of profits which were severely curtailed by Lord Cornwallis' sweeping financial and administrative reforms, but his personal relations with the authorities at Calcutta were always of the best. It was at this time that he began seriously to consider retiring from Jan Compagnie's service and investing his capital in an annuity in

[1] Cf. Hickey's *Memoirs*, III, 285–6; IV, 29, 160–1; C. R. Boxer, *The Mandarin at Chinsura. Isaac Titsingh in Bengal, 1785–1792*, (Mededeling No. LXXXIV of The Royal Institute for the Indies, Amsterdam, 1949).

[2] Holden Furber, *John Company at work* (Harvard University Press, 1948) pp. 78–109, 153–9. It may be added that some of Titsingh's mss. on Japan, China, and Bengal are included in the "Macartney Papers" of the Wason collection at Cornell University. For his mss. at Batavia, cf. Wynaendts van Resandt, 173–4.

English funds. The outbreak of the French Revolution and the rapid deterioration of the situation in Europe caused him to delay his departure, which was also postponed at the earnest request of the Governor-General and Council at Batavia [1].

Titsingh was on excellent terms with his colleagues and superiors at Batavia, but the same cannot be said of his relations with the Board of Directors in Holland. He ascribed the "groundless aspersions" and "baseless insinuations" which the *Heeren Seventien* made against him in their correspondence with Batavia, to the machinations of a disgruntled ex-subordinate named Falck. A cantankerous critic named Eilbrecht also gave him a good deal of trouble until transferred to Negapatam; but although Titsingh once termed the little Dutch colony at Chinsura an "adders' nest" in a moment of exasperation, he was clearly and deservedly popular with the majority of his compatriots. His long-delayed departure from Bengal in March 1792, was made the occasion not only of spontaneous demonstrations of goodwill by the Hollanders at Chinsura, but of official and private appreciation of his conduct and character by the English at Calcutta.

Letters from Batavia had warned Titsingh that the city was in a sorry plight, but even so, he was appalled at the conditions he found there after his seven years absence. Contrasting them with those obtaining on his first arrival in Java nearly thirty years previously, he wrote, "Batavia was then full of well-to-do citizens and respectable merchants, all of whom were cheerful and happy, whilst credit was generally good, and a spirit of energy universally prevailed. Nowadays there are hardly four burghers who are worthy of the name of merchants, the colony is bereft of its European inhabitants in comparison with former years, and the severe business depression has made the few remaining capitalists very chary of investing their money. This in turn worsens the general depression and everything is failing rapidly."

---

[1] Cf. Holden Furber, *loc. cit.*, and Kalinkar Datta, *The Dutch in Bengal and Bihar* (University of Patna Press, 1948) pp. 143–147. For a discussion of Cornwallis' reforms see A. Aspinall, *Cornwallis in Bengal. The administrative and judicial reforms of Lord Cornwallis in Bengal, 1786–1793*, (Manchester, 1931).

The sole remedy for the economic crisis, in his view, was
to make Batavia an open port where foreigners and natives
could trade on the same terms as the Dutch, in much the
same way as English Calcutta had achieved such pheno-
menal prosperity. Incidentally, in marked contrast to the
majority of his countrymen (as, for instance, Dirk van
Hogendorp in his *Berigt*) and to Raffles two decades later,
Titsingh had a good word to say for the Chinese mercantile
community in Java whom he considered to be a useful and
peaceful folk [1].

Social life at Batavia had naturally deteriorated under
these adverse conditions. Most of the large town houses,
formerly owned by Hollanders, were either empty or else
served as tenements for Chinese, Javanese or Malays. Fever
and malaria, to say nothing of gin and brandy, took a heavy
toll of the few European survivors, the annual death-rate at
Batavia during this period being probably the highest in the
world. Titsingh was appointed a fully-fledged Councillor of
India on his arrival, and was kept very busy in picking up
the arrears of routine administration, apart from shouldering
a good deal of extra work. This, however, as he frankly
acknowledged, was probably a blessing in disguise, since he
was always an enemy to sloth, and his continual activity
helped him to keep fit. He did not neglect his books, passing
long hours shut up in his library with the Japanese and
Chinese collections which he had formed. He admits to
finding Batavian society very formal and boring after the
more cosmopolitan life which he had enjoyed in Bengal.
Still, he did not lead the life of a recluse, as he sometimes
spent an evening with a few congenial friends at Molenvliet
or at Jacatara, whilst Wednesdays and Saturdays were passed
in the company of Governor-General Alting. Ever a bache-
lor at heart, he brusquely rejected the direct and indirect
advances of a wealthy widow named Keijser, — "I received
flowers, but threw them in the piss-pot," he notes laconically
in one of his letters.

The outbreak of war with Revolutionary France was

---

[1] This account of Titsingh's life at Batavia in 1792–3, is taken from his letters to
his brother and friends in Europe during this period, as copied in his letter-book in
the British Museum (*Additional Mss.* 18101).

another nail in the coffin of Jan Compagnie in the East, and
the Java Sea was soon infested with French privateers based
on the island of Mauritius. The death-rate at Batavia was so
high, that great difficulty was experienced in finding a crew
for even a solitary homeward-bound Indiaman, and Dutch
naval strength was now negligible. Under the circumstances,
the Batavian Government appealed for help to Lord Cornwallis, "whose noble character and unbounded dislike of
the French is our only hope of support". A preliminary
refusal was later redeemed by the dispatch of five armed
English East-Indiamen who cleared the straits of Sunda
and Malacca of the French corsairs. Titsingh was kept busy
in entertaining the English officers and crews during the
squadron's visit to Batavia, and despite all difficulties managed to fit out two Dutch vessels to co-operate with them [1].

On the 5th March 1793, Lord Macartney arrived at Batavia on his way to China as ambassador to the court of the
Emperor Ch'ien-lung, with the ships *Lion* and *Hindostan*.
As the only member of the Council who spoke English,
Titsingh was deputed to act as cicerone to the ambassadorial
party, — a task which he found most exacting, as he had to
be with them continuously, and was suffering from a severe
bout of fever at the time. He was frankly relieved when
Lord Macartney fell ill with a violent attack of the gout —
probably owing to the gargantuan banquets provided, which
exceeded even Bengal hospitality — and was forced to re-
embark before the departure of the ships on the 17th March.
Titsingh was rightly sceptical of the English chances of
success, and foresaw not only that Peking mandarindom but
that the other Europeans at Canton would intrigue against
the embassy, "out of suspicion that its real objective was to
monopolise the China trade and get possession of one of the
islands near Macao for the English. This would open the
door for their invasion of China within a few years, whilst
their ambitious and enterprising character is but too well-
known throughout Asia." Little did Titsingh think when
he penned these lines to his brother in April 1793, that

---

[1] The English squadron, under the command of Captain Mitchell, comprised the
William Pitt (44), *Britannia* (44), *Houghton* (40), *Nonsuch* (36), and the cutter *Nau-
tilius* (10). They captured the French privateers *Le Vengeur* (38) and *La Resolue* (26).

within eighteen months he himself would be heading a Dutch embassy to the Court of Ch'ien-lung which was to prove an even greater failure than Macartney's mission.

It is at first sight strange that the Dutch dispatched an embassy to Peking at a time when Macartney had just left the country empty-handed, when Jan Compagnie was on the verge of dissolution, and when Holland itself was on the point of being engulfed by the surge of revolutionary fever from France. The man who was chiefly responsible for this surprising resolution was the chief of the Dutch factory at Canton, Andreas Everardus van Braam Houckgeest, to whom we likewise owe the best published accounts of the embassy. The details of Van Braam's curious and chequered career in Europe, America and Asia can be read in the excellent account of his biographer, Professor J. L. Duyvendak. I shall therefore confine myself here to a brief consideration of this last Dutch embassy to the Manchu Court as it affected Titsingh more particularly [1].

It seems that Van Braam had long cherished the idea of proceeding to Peking as an ambassador or representative of his employers, and the fact that Macartney's mission had ended in failure apparently increased rather than damped his ardour. At any rate, seizing on the palpably flimsy pretext that the Cantonese authorities had suggested to the English the desirability of sending an embassy to congratulate the Emperor on the sixtieth anniversary of his reign, Van Braam wrote to his superiors at Batavia urging them to do likewise. In this project he was aided and abetted by some of the high officials at Canton, who for reasons of their own were desirous of producing at Court a suitably docile and obedient foreign embassy which would counteract any awkward after-thoughts which Macartney's mission might have inspired. In spite of the improbability of the English sending another embassy so soon after Macartney's

[1] J. L. Duyvendak, *The Last Dutch Embassy to the Chinese Court* (1794–1795), in *T'oung Pao*, Vol. XXXIV, pp. 1–137 (Leiden, 1938); *The Last Dutch Embassy in the "Veritable Records"* (ibidem, 223–227); *Supplementary Documents on the last Dutch Embassy to the Chinese Court*, in *T'oung Pao*, XXXV, 329–353. (Leiden, 1940). C. R. Boxer, *Isaac Titsingh's Embassy to the Court of Ch'ien-lung, 1794–1795*, in *T'ien ' Hsia*, Vol. VIII, pp. 9–33 (Shanghai, 1939). British Museum, *Additional Mss.*, 18101, fls. 136–186. What follows is taken from one or another of these sources.

fiasco, Alting and his council surprisingly accepted van
Braam's assertions at their face value and resolved on the
dispatch of a mission as suggested by him. They did not,
however, select van Braam as ambassador, as he had hoped
they would do, but persuaded Isaac Titsingh to accept
the post on his own — and most advantageous — terms.
Van Braam was appointed second, with full powers to take
Titsingh's place if he fell sick or died.

Sailing from Batavia on 15th August, 1794, in the *Siam*,
Titsingh arrived off the Bocca Tigris a month later. Here he
was met by van Braam, who sprang the news on him that
no other nations were sending a congratulatory mission save
the Dutch. Considerably taken aback by this information,
especially after van Braam's previous assurances to the contrary, Titsingh had thoughts of abandoning the project
and returning to Batavia, but soon made up his mind to go
through with it. His reasons for this decision are not very far
to seek. Like van Braam, he was a great admirer and student
of Far Eastern culture, and he was fully aware that it
was the lot of few to go to Peking. At the earnest entreaty of
the authorities at Batavia, he had postponed the taking
effect of his resignation from the Company's service until
after he had performed this last duty, and it would have
been too much of an anti-climax to return from Canton to
Batavia. Most persons in his place would have acted in the
same way, and he can hardly be blamed for suppressing
any belated misgivings which he might have felt about
the embassy, in his anxiety to get to Peking at all costs.

This anxiety is quite obvious in the accounts of both
Titsingh and van Braam, and was no doubt largely responsible for their making two grave errors of judgement in their
dealings with the officials at Canton, which had unfavourable
repercussions on the embassy later. The first of these was
to promise that the embassy had not the slightest intention
of making any requests or lodging any complaints, but that
it was simply and solely intended as a congratulatory mission on the occasion of the Emperor's jubilee. The second
mistake was an assurance given to the Viceroy that the
ambassadors were prepared to leave Canton in time to
reach Peking by the Chinese New Year, thus exposing

themselves to the hardship of travelling through the interior of China at the coldest and most inclement season of the year. Titsingh admits in his own account that he lightheartedly assented to this proposition, in the belief that it was impossible for the court of Peking to confirm this suggestion, owing to the great distance from Canton and the short time available for the messengers to go and return [1].

The ambassadorial cortege when it finally left the City of Rams on 22nd November 1794, was composed of some twenty-seven persons, apart from the conducting mandarins. The first part of the journey was done in boats, and the real hardships of the trip began when the overland journey started at a place opposite Nanchang, the capital of Kiangsi province. Professor Duyvendak has ably summarised the latter part of the journey as follows. "The two ambassadors travelled in chairs, the other gentlemen on horseback, but soon the train with the luggage could not keep up with them, so that they had to spend the nights without their beds, on bare boards, without proper food and even without wine, in lodging houses that frequently were indescribably bad. Three hundred coolies were required for the transport and these, being insufficiently paid by greedy officials, sometimes refused to move. Such heavy work was demanded from them that eight of them died of exhaustion. It was difficult to procure fresh coolies because the train that transported the 'tribute presents' was just ahead, and for these not less than one thousand coolies were employed. On Christmas Eve the ambassadors overtook the train with the four mirrors destined for the Emperor, each carried by 24 coolies, followed by a relay of 24 others. The journey more and more resembled a forced march. The conducting mandarins' sole fear was lest they should arrive too late in Peking and scant regard was paid to the comfort of the party. The last eighteen days, daily distances of 120–180 *li* were covered; there were early starts and late arrivals in the severest weather. Recriminations were frequent but of little avail.

[1] In connection with this embassy some remarkably quick times were made by various couriers between Canton and Peking, one letter taking only twelve days, apparently a record. Cf. Professor Duyvendak's note in *T'oung Pao*, XXXV, 333 (Leiden, 1940).

The conductors disclaimed all responsibility for the insufficient preparations made locally for receiving the ambassadors but sometimes they succeeded in monopolizing the better accommodation for themselves. On December 13th. Titsingh notes his regret ever to have been persuaded to undertake this embassy" [1].

The climax of discomfort was reached just when the ambassadors had every right to expect that they could at length enjoy a decent lodging and a bed, namely on the night of their arrival at Peking. They entered the capital on 9th January, 1795, on the eve of the "closing of the seals", passing into the Tartar City through the Hsuan-wu gate at 5.30 p.m. Before they had gone much further, they were halted, then turned round, and carried outside the gate, which was immediately shut behind them. They were therefore compelled to spend the night in a miserable cart-driver's tavern in the Chinese city, sleeping in their clothes and without anything to eat save a handful of stale biscuts which young de Guignes chanced to have in his pocket. Small wonder that they were all highly incensed at this outrageous treatment, and that Titsingh wrote in his Journal, "even Mr. van Braam, fond though he is of the Chinese, declared that if he could have suspected the least of these vile treatments, he would never have put down one word in favour of sending an embassy" [2].

Despite the rigours of their trip, and their routine of starting before dawn and arriving long after nightfall, several members of the embassy kept voluminous diaries of their journey and faithfully entered therein all they saw and heard of note. The journals of van Braam and de Guignes (son of Titsingh's Parisian correspondent) are available in print, but Titsingh's manuscript is still unpublished. All three were cultured and much-travelled men, but Professor Duyvendak, who has compared their respective accounts, is convinced that van Braam's version is the best. This may be so, but it would be interesting to have Titsingh's journal

[1] Duyvendak in *T'oung Pao*, XXXIV, 43–4. Cf. also Van Braam, *Voyage de l'ambassade* (2 vols. Philadelphia, 1797–1798), I, 90–100. There were three conductng mandarins, two Chinese and a Manchu.

[2] Duyvendak, *op. cit*, p. 44; van Braam, *op cit*. p. 133–4; de Guignes, *Voyage à Peking*, (Paris 1808), p. 357–8.

printed, since he was one of the very few Europeans who had the opportunity of visiting the capitals of both China and Japan before the second half of the nineteenth century [1].

Titsingh's first audience with the Emperor took place on 12th January, and his reception did not fill him with transports of delight. Apart from kowtowing to Ch'ien-lung himself, the Dutch envoys had to do likewise when "the Emperor sent us from his table yellow porcelain saucers with small cakes, for which we did obeisance; shortly afterwards he sent again a dish with pieces of game, looking as if they were remnants of gnawed bones. They were dumped on the table, but it required another obeisance. Although this was a visible token of his (the Emperor's) affection, it furnished the most conclusive proof of coarseness and lack of civilization. However incredible this may seem in Europe, it is too remarkable to pass over in silence. From the reports with which the missionaries have deluded the world for a number of years, I had imagined a very civilized and enlightened people. These ideas were deeply rooted and a kind of violence was necessary to eradicate them, but this reception, joined to all our previous experiences was a radical cure". [2]

Titsingh's indignation is quite understandable, but on the other hand it was perhaps rather rash of him to condemn Chinese civilization out of hand, simply because the Imperial leavings which he received bore the marks of the Emperor's teeth and good appetite. As Professor Duyvendak points out, the status of the ambassadors as tribute-bearers being admitted and properly understood, the treatment received at Court (as apart from that on the journey) was throughout extremely gracious. They were received, both publicly and privately, much more frequently than had been the case with any other Western embassies, Macartney's included; and they appear to have been the only foreigners ever allowed to witness the Imperial Procession on its way to the Temple of Heaven, which they did on the 27th January, 1795. Even Titsingh was delighted

---

[1] Perhaps his only predecessor in this respect was the Portuguese Jesuit, Padre João Rodriguez Tçuzzu (1561–1634), who visited Kyoto, Yedo and Peking in the first half of the seventeenth century.

[2] Titsingh's mss. journal apud Duyvendak, *op. cit.* pp. 53–57.

with a visit to the summer palace at Yuan, where they were taken to see the view from the Emperor's favourite cabinet in his private apartments. "Never did I see a more enchanting spot, either in reality or in picture," wrote Titsingh in his journal, "all the picturesqueness so much admired in Chinese paintings was realised here in the highest degree. One was completely transported by the beauty."

Nevertheless, despite this and a few other such welcome interludes in the dreary round of early rising and frequent performance of the "three kneelings and the nine head knockings", it was without regret that Titsingh and his companions left Peking for Canton on the 15th February 1795, after their farewell audience a week earlier. Quite apart from the fact that they had pleasant spring weather for their return journey, they were now much better treated by their conductors and by the local officials. The reason for this greatly improved treatment is explained in an Imperial circular-edict promulgated on the 24th December 1794, which Professor Duyvendak has printed in full. This edict frankly admits that Macartney's embassy had been much more honourably treated on its journey to Peking, and it goes on to say that "in as much as no banquets have been prepared for this ambassador [Titsingh] and his suite in the provinces through which they passed on the road, different treatments have been meted out to two exactly identical cases of Tribute Ambassadors from Western countries. Thus we have failed in a worthy behaviour for China, and the said Tribute Ambassador and his suite on perceiving this are bound to feel somewhat disappointed. Now not only will this Ambassador and his suite from their arrival in the Capital onwards without exception be liberally bestowed and rewarded, but moreover orders are herewith given to transmit this Edict to all the Viceroys concerned, that in future, when the said ambassador and his suite will pass through their territory on the return journey, banquets shall be given in their honour in accordance with the precedent of the treatment of the English ambassador." As Professor Duyvendak points out, this document is, in a very real sense, an apology to the Dutch embassy for the lack of courtesy shown it on the hurried journey to Peking.

Whether the interesting and comparatively leisurely three months journey from Peking to Canton in the spring of 1795, largely effaced the memories of the previous winter's hardships, or whether (as is more likely) Titsingh wished to save his "face" with the outer world, he professed himself after his return to Canton as fully satisfied with the treatment which he had experienced.

His letters to his family and friends make no reference to Ch'ien-lung's gift of half-gnawed bones, nor to the wearisome formalities of the kowtow. On the contrary, he writes to his London agents, Messrs. Paxton, two days after his return to Canton, — "I was treated with every possible mark of distinction, constantly attending all the festivals at Court and at the Emperor's country-seat where I passed eight days. I arrived at Peking the 9th of January, and left it the 15th February extremely satisfied of [*sic*] my reception." This tendentious account might be explained as due to his unwillingness to expose the earlier treatment accorded him to the derision of the English, but the same reason hardly applies to the version which he wrote to his uncle and aunt in Holland. "I have completed my embassy with all possible satisfaction, having been received by the Emperor with the greatest politeness and distinction, and enjoyed more tokens of his princely kindness than any previous European ambassador can boast of. The journey to Court was painful on account of the excessive haste to reach Peking in the biting cold; but the return journey, through the scenic beauties of the fairest provinces, was thus all the more pleasant". His real sentiments are probably more accurately reflected in the closing lines of the French transcription of his China journal, –

"nous voilà délivré de tous les mandarins, *favente deo,*
illi robur et aes triplex
circa pectus erat
qui le premier dans ces pais sauvages
eut le desir de voir de stupides visages" [1].

---

[1] B. M. *Add. Mss.* 18102. Professor Duyvendak points out (*T'oung Pao*, XXXIV, 102–4) that one reason why this Dutch embassy had such a "bad press" in Europe, was that, through a curious chain of unfortunate events, it was only known in various pirated and truncated editions. These omitted the latter and more successful part

(By the favour of God his heart was encased in oak and bronze who first wanted to look at silly faces in these out-landish countries). [1]

At Canton, Titsingh received the disagreeable tidings of the death of his brother and of the revolution in Holland, the subsequent flight of the Stadthouder to England, and the conquest of the Netherlands by the French. Under these circumstances, it was almost impossible for him to return direct to Holland, as Dutch shipping had practically vanished off the face of the seven seas. He therefore resolved to per-severe in his original intention of retiring to England to settle down. The fact that Holland and England were then at war was not such an obstacle as it would be in these sup-posedly more enlightened days. In order to avoid putting all his eggs in one basket, Titsingh embarked some of his possessions, including the presents he had received from Ch'ien-lung, in the neutral Spanish ship *Purissima Concepcion*, through the influence of his friend, Don Manuel de Agote, the Philippine Company's agent at Macao. His natural son, Willem, sailed in a Swedish ship which left Canton in January 1796. Two months later Titsingh himself embarked in the East-Indiaman *Circencester*, Captain Lind-say, which weighed anchor in the Pearl River on the 20th March. He had paid £ 300 for the cost of his own passage and that of his servant, together with his luggage, "which is very voluminous, and all my library"[2].

After a long and stormy passage, the *Cirencester* dropped anchor in the Downs on the 11th December 1796. Titsingh disembarked at once and took a post-chaise for London, where he stayed at Latham's Hotel, Albermarle Street. He lost no time in calling upon his old friends of Bengal and China days, receiving a warm welcome from Lord Macartney (then on the point of leaving for Cape Colony) and the sino-

of the embassy, as related in the original but very rare two-volume Philadalphia edition of 1797–8.

[1] I am indebted to my colleague, Professor W. S. Maguinness M. A., for identifying this quotation from Horace's *Odes*.

[2] War having broken out between England and Spain, the *Purissima Concepcion* was taken by the English off her home-port of Cadiz. Titsingh's son, Willem, stayed for some months at Capetown before returning to Europe.

logue Sir George Staunton. The hospitality shown him by his English friends did not cause him to forget the fate of his compatriots in Asia, — "my heart is still too devoted to India to enable me to remain indifferent to their fate", as he wrote to his friend (and successor), Van Cittters, in Bengal.

Thirty-two years in the East and the long passage home round the Cape, had made an unfavourable impression on even Titsingh's robust constitution, which was aggravated by the chilly gloom of a London winter. He was advised and accordingly resolved to take the waters at Bath, which he did, returning to London in February. His letters continue to bear witness to the hospitality which his English friends delighted to show him, and he made a passing resolution to settle in the West Country near Bath. But the natural love of his own land, and a longing to see his relatives again, gradually overcame his earlier determination never to return to Holland.

In 1801, he crossed over to the Netherlands, but evidently not without some unpleasant experience at the hands of the officials of the Aliens Office. He did not find in Holland the peaceful and studious life which he craved. Apart from the disturbed political situation in the Batavian Republic, his father and brother were dead, and the general atmosphere was wholly unpropitious for the publication of his works. He therefore removed to Paris, where he had the congenial company of fellow Orientalists, such as the younger de Guignes, Klaproth, and Rémusat. From here he made frequent trips to Holland, and kept up a close correspondence with his English friends. His greatest friend was William Marsden, the famous Malay scholar, then secretary of the Board of Admiralty, to whom he sent the English translations of his works as he finished them.

Writing to Marsden in 1807, he observes that he would very much like to make another trip to England, but the fear of getting into "some serious scrape" with the Aliens Office on his return, prevents it. He is pessimistic about the chances of getting his Sino-Japanese translations published in Holland, where Arts and Sciences are at a discount, and novels or suchlike the only books which sell, — "voilà ou la fraternité nous a reduite", as he expresses himself to a French correspondent in the same year. Evidently, however, he found that this was one of the things which they did not order much better in France. When forwarding to Marsden the English translation of his Sino-Japanese chronology in June, 1807, he writes, — "It was on the advice of Mr. de Volney I declin'd having the French translation printed at Paris, in order not to be exposed to the many vexations and impositions of that covetous sort of people .... besides I desired it might previously appear in England". This translation, incidentally, was dedicated to his old friend, Kuchiki Samon Masatsuna, daimyo of Fukuchiyama (Tamba) being dated Amsterdam, 11th June, 1807.

Two years later, Titsingh sent Marsden from Amsterdam the draft of his French transcript of the anecdotal history of the Emperors (Dairi) and Shoguns of Japan. In his covering letter he refers to the "tedious task of translating the Chronicle of the Dayris, which fills 500 pages in great folio, a task I will never have the courage to undertake at Paris, by the variety of distractions, constantly to be met with, — here, where the principal object is how best to kill time, it is the proper spot". This work he likewise dedicated to Kuchiki Samon. In this same latter he alludes to his excellent health, but adds that he was pushing on with his work as fast as possible, since he ardently desired to finish the translation of all the materials which he had collected concerning Japan. In June 1811, Titsingh sent Marsden the English draft of his essay on Japanese marriage and funeral ceremonies, as also a topographical description of the island of Yezo (Hokkaido), but within a year he was dead. It can be said without exaggeration that it was no ordinary dilettante who breathed his last at Paris on 9th February 1812, after a short but painful illness, but one of the most learned men of his time [1].

Having thus attempted a sketch of Isaac Titsingh's career, a few words may be devoted to his position as an

[1] Foregoing from B. M. *Additional Mss.* 18101, 9390 and 9391. Cf. also *Asiatic Review*, Vol. VIII, (May-August, 1832), pp. 17–30.

Orientalist, and above all to his standing as a Japanologue. In estimating his abilities in this connection, it is essential to take into consideration the state of knowledge about the Far East in general and Japan in particular during his lifetime, as well as the work his of predecessors.

In comparing his achievements with those of the other servants of the Dutch East India Company in Japan, he may be fairly termed the most learned of all the Hollanders who visited that country during the two centuries and a half in which Jan Compagnie frequented Hirado and Deshima. The only ones who can be compared with him in this respect are François Caron, Johannes Camphuis, Engelbert Kaempfer, Hendrik Doeff and Philip Franz Von Siebold. Of these, Kaempfer and Von Siebold were Germans, and Caron a naturalised Frenchman; so although their work in different ways was undoubtedly greater than Titsingh's, it does not affect his claim to be regarded as the most successful Hollander. Camphuis and Doeff did useful work in their day and generation, both culturally and politically, but neither their researches nor what they bequeathed to posterity rank so high as Titsingh's in this respect.

Again, it is noteworthy that Titsingh has a double claim to fame as an interpreter of Japan to Europe, as also of Europe to Japan. It is on the former account that such posthumous renown as he enjoys is based, but it may be doubted whether his influence was not really greater and more lasting in the latter aspect. When Titsingh came to Japan, Dutch — and hence European — prestige was at an exceedingly low ebb, despite the favourable impression that Thunberg had made in learned society a few years before, and despite the existence of a definite liberal feeling in several quarters. During his three years in the country, Titsingh not only gained for his employers unlooked-for commercial advantages at a very critical time, but he greatly strengthened the cultural approach of Japan to the West. The books he brought, the ideas he exchanged, the keen interest he took in things Japanese, all contributed powerfully to spread a more exact and attractive knowledge of the West in the minds of the most sensitive and intelligent Japanese. This favourable impression was never effaced, and the friends he made in high places subsequently proved themselves to be the most influential exponents of the move towards opening the country, which, despite temporary setbacks, gathered increasing momentum during the early XIXth century.

As regards the value of the other side of Titsingh's work, namely his worth as an interpreter of Japan to Europe, his friend, Sir William Jones, was not guilty of more than pardonable exaggeration when he addressed the Asiatic Society of Bengal on the subject in 1790, as follows, — "Kaempfer has taken from Mr. Titsingh the honour of being the first, and he from Kaempfer that of being the only European, who, by a long residence in Japan, and a familiar intercourse with the principal natives of it, has been able to collect authentick materials for the natural and civil history of a country secluded, as the Romans used to say of our own island, from the rest of the world. The works of these illustrious travellers will confirm and embelish each other; and when Mr. Titsingh shall have acquired a knowledge of Chinese, to which a part of his leisure in Java will be devoted, his precious collection of books in that language, on the laws, and revolutions, the natural productions, the arts, manufactures and sciences of Japan, will be in his hands an inexhaustible mine of new and important information" [1].

Unfortunately for Titsingh's posthumous fame, he was unable, after leaving to Japan, to find competent Chinese or Japanese scholars who could help him to translate all the works which he had collected. His own knowledge of Sino-Japanese written characters was clearly small, although he apparently had a fair knowledge of the spoken language, at any rate when he left Japan in 1784. Owing to his own roving career and the disturbed condition of Europe, he was able to do little more than polish and edit the translations which had been prepared under his supervision at Deshima. Even so, a good deal of material was ready for the press in three languages (Dutch, English and French) at the time of

[1] *Asiatick Researches*, Vol. II, pp. 379–380 (Calcutta, 1790). Jones forgot to mention (or did not know of) the early Jr uit missionaries in Japan, the Englishman Will Adams, and the Fleming François Caron, as Titsingh's predecessors.

his death. What appeared in print posthumously was only a small part of what was actually prepared; and part of this was mangled and deformed by his editors and publishers. This was, in some degree, the fault of his natural son, Willem, whom he had taken good care to legitimise and educate in Holland, after overcoming his early reluctance to acknowledge him openly. The editor of the *Asiatic Journal* (May, 1832) informs us that "this wretched young man was able so expeditiously to dissipate his inheritance at the gambling-table and in the society of a female opera-dancer, that, only two years after his father's death, he was forced to dispose of, for trifling considerations, the collections and manuscripts which had cost so much toil and expense to accumulate."

Other early nineteenth-century authorities, such as Rémusat, Klaproth, and Hildreth, are inclined to belittle the value of his work, and term his contributions to Japanese history *jejeune*. Von Siebold, on the other hand, stigmatizes Rémusat and Klaproth as Titsingh's "illegitimate literary heirs;" whilst James Murdoch in the present century also rates Titsingh's achievement very highly. More competent judges of Japan and the Japanese than these two eminent *savants*, both of whom lived long in the country, it would be hard to find. Like Siebold, Titsingh managed to smuggle out of the country tracings of Japanese maps and charts which he had copied in secrecy at Deshima. If these were lost or destroyed after his death, that was no fault of his. He states that his own standard of careful accuracy in translation and transcription was modelled on that of his friend, Kuchiki Samon, who, after discovering some minor errors in a numismatic work he had written, called in all copies and burnt them, supplying their owners with a new and corrected edition.

To gain a fair impression of the real value of Titsingh's work as a pioneer Japanologue, it is necessary to consult his manuscripts in the British Museum, as well as his posthumously printed works. Anyone who does this, will find that many subjects which are usually considered to have been first discussed in the *Transactions of the Asiatic Society of Japan*, or some such learned periodical, were dealt with by Isaac Titsingh a century and half ago. As an instance of this, we may mention Professor Basil Hall Chamberlain's charming essay on *Basho and the Japanese Epigram*, where it is stated that the first European author to deal with Japanese epigrammatic verse was W. G. Aston in his *Grammar of the Japanese written Language*, published in 1877. Yet Titsingh had translated some typical stanzas into elegant Latin verse nearly a hundred years before. A number of these translations together with a brief essay by him on the nature of Japanese poetry, were published in his posthumous *Illustrations of Japan* [1].

In conclusion, when apprising the value of Titsingh's work as a Japanologue, it is only fair to judge his achievements by the standard he set himself, which is aptly described in one of his letters to Marsden in these terms, — "in order to form a proper idea of the spirit, the character, and the customs of a nation, almost unknown in Europe, I deemed it preferable to represent them in their own dress ... to obtain this end, I applied during my stay in Japan to some friends, reputed as men of learning, and free from all National prejudices; they procured me such works on various topicks, as enjoyed with them the highest regard; having succeded in this, a litteral translation appeared to me more congenial with the purpose, and likely to be more satisfactory to the desire for more distinct notions on a people almost unknown, though fully deserving the attention, since a number of years so profusely lavished on the Chinese". That he succeeded in this praiseworthy aim, no careful reader of his surviving works can deny; and it is a great pity that this learned Orientalist and honourable man did not live to publish all the valuable materials which he had so carefully amassed, and whereby he might have received his due from posterity.

---

[1] Not that Titsingh was the first European author to translate Japanese verse, as I erroneously stated in the 1936 edition of this book. This honour belongs to the Portuguese Jesuit Padre, João Rodriguez (Tçuzzu), who published an essay on the subject and some translations of classical and colloquial verse on fls. 181–194 of his *Arte da Lingoa de Iapam* (Nagasaki, 1604–1608).

TITSINGH'S MANUSCRIPTS IN THE BRITISH MUSEUM

Add. 18098 List of places and geographical names in the island(s) of Japan. Paper. XVIIIth cent. 1 vol. folio.

Add. 18099 List of Daimyo with their incomes fl. 29ff.
List of Japanese Emperors and Shoguns from beginning of 17th to beginning of 18th century, fl. 61 ff. — Further lists of Daimyo, temples etc. 62 ff. — Names of streets in Nagasaki. 1 vol. folio. In Dutch.

Add. 18100 Copies of Japanese inscriptions from seals etc. — fl. 1. Inlyding tot de beschrijving van het naalde steeken en moxa branden, in verscheide ziektens etc. fl. 6. Aanteekeningen omtrent de Dayris ofte oppervorsten, en de sjogoons of krons bevelhebberen; beneevens het jaarlijks ceremonieel in het Paleis te Yedo; de vijf groote Feest of compliment daagen, en het Feest der Lantaarns. 1 vol. folio. In Dutch.

Add. 18101 Titsingh's Letter-book, 16.i.1790–28.iv.1797.
Copies of letters written bij him whilst Governor of Chinsura, Councillor at Batavia, and Ambassador in China, and whilst in England to his relatives and friends. 1 vol. folio. 204 pp. In Dutch & English.

Add. 18102 Journal d'un voyage à Peking traduit du hollandais et du manuscript autographe de M. Titzingh. 22.xi.1794–11.v.1795. 1 vol. folio. 442 pp., of which several blank. In French.

Add. 9390 Letters of Titsingh to Marsden, 1806–1811. Amsterdam, Paris, Copenhagen, etc. Very interesting. Last letter dated Amsterdam, June 1811. 1 vol. folio; about 50 pp. In English.

Add. 9391–6 Notes on Sino-Japanese Chronology. 9391, *Chronology of the Japanese etc.* is dedicated to Marsden and dated Amsterdam 31.iii.1804. 6 volumes. folio. In English.

Add. 9397 Description of wedding ceremonies, funerals etc. in Japan. Fl. 1–60. Two descriptions of the island of Yezo. 1 vol. folio.

N.B. For the titles of some unpublished mss. of Titsingh in the archives at Batavia, cf. Wijnaendts van Resandt, *De Gezaghebbers der OIC,* (Amsterdam, 1944), 173–4. Mr. W. van Resandt is mistaken in his assertion that the *Memorie van overgave* of Deshima to Romberg in 1783 has been printed.

TITSINGH'S PRINTED WORKS

1. *Cérémonies usitées au Japon pour les Mariages et les Funérailles.* (Paris, 1819). With Atlas of Plates.
2. *Mémoires et Anecdotes sur la dynastie régnante des Djogouns.* (Paris, 1820; edited by Abel Rémusat). These two works were translated into English under the title of
3. *Illustrations of Japan.* (London, 1822). With coloured plates after the Japanese originals. A Dutch translation appeared three years later. —
4. *Bijzonderheden over Japan.* ('s-Gravenhage, 1824–25). 2 volumes.
5. *Nipon O Dai Itsi ran, ou Annales des Empereurs du Japon.* Revised and edited by Klaproth. (Paris, 1834). This volume was printed for the Oriental Translation Fund of Great Britain and Ireland.
6. *Déscription de la Terre Yeso traduite du Japonais* par M.T. (in *Annales des Voyages.* Vol. XXIV. Paris, 1814).
7. *Bereiding van Saké en Soya.* (in Vol. 3 of the *Verhandelingen van het Bataviaasch Genootschap,* Batavia, 1781).

Further bio-bibliographical notices of Titsingh's works will be found in the following,
8. Charpentier-Cossigny (ed.) *Voyage au Bengale,* I. pp. 245–286. (*Notice sur le Japon par le citoyen* . . . .). Paris, An 7 (1799).
9. Abel Rémusat, — *Nouvelles Mélanges Asiatiques.* II. pp. 266–282. (*Sur une collection d'ouvrages relatifs au Japon formée par Titsingh*). (Paris, 1829).
11. *Asiatic Review,* Vol. VIII (May-August, 1832) pp. 17–30.
12. *Het Instituut, of verslagen en mededeelingen.* (uitgeg. door de vier klassen v. h. Kon. Ned. Instituut, 1841). Article by Professor Den Tex, blz. 227–233.
13. *Handelingen en geschriften van het Indisch Genootschap te 's-Gravenhage,* VII. (1860) p. 303.
14. *Bibliotheca Japonica.* Par Henri Cordier. (Paris, 1912). A very full bibliographical collation of Titsingh's printed works will be found in columns 448–451, 458, 465 and 471 of this excellent work.
15. C. R. BOXER, *"The Mandarin at Chinsura". Isaac Titsingh in Bengal,* 1785–1792, (Koninklijke Vereeniging Indisch Instituut, Mededeling No. LXXXIV, Afdeling Volkenkunde No. 32, Amsterdam, 1949).

APPENDIX I

Oranda (proper name, *Holland*).

Is situated 57 (some say 53) degrees from the North Pole, and lies 12,900 *ri* overseas from Japan, in a N.W. direction from China and Japan. This country is properly called Holland, and consists of a union of 7 provincies, of which Holland is one. [The others are] Zeeland, Groningen, Utrecht, Gelderland, Overijssel, Friesland, and Holland [sic]. The foregoing seven provinces are of about the same area as the province of Kyushu in Japan, and are ruled by 4 persons, who formed a Company and dispatched merchant ships to various countries; these 4 rulers are called *Compania*, and as these various countries lie at a great distance from the mainland, they have placed a *Daikwan* [*lit*. Regent or Commissioner] in Karabaya [Java] who is charged with sending the merchant ships to Japan and other places [1] This *daikwan* is termed General, and he keeps the accounts of the trade driven with these various countries, forwarding a general summary of the whole to the *Compania* once in every 15 years so it is said. [Holland] is a very cold country throughout all four seasons of the year. In the sea to the North of this land, there lies a country called Land of Night, at about 2,000 *ri* from Holland. It is said that the inhabitants have one eye and a mouth in the top of their heads, whilst there are some regions quite uninhabited. In these countries it is broad daylight for six months, and night for the other six months, and only one day in a year is it night and day in the normal way. The cold is very severe, and during the night season of the year, the whole surface of the sea is frozen, and it only thaws a little in the daylight season of the year [2]. It is said that there are similar countries which are visited by the Hollanders.

The Hollanders have white skins, red and short hair, high noses

[1] The reader no doubt will readily perceive that the V.O.C. is confused with the States-General, and that the *Daikwan* is the Governor-General at Batavia.

[2] Probably derived from mariners' yarns about Greenland and Spitzbergen.

and the pupils of their eyes are white. Their clothes are usually made of woollen cloth, whilst both high and low alike wear beaver hats. Whenever they salute each other, they always remove their hats. The garments of those of high rank are beautifully decorated with gold and silver; and they wear swords suspended from [a belt over] the shoulder. Every year they go to pay their respects to the Yedo government, as you can see. Their language is quite distinct from that of India and other [Asiatic] countries, and resembles the Barbarian tongue, for they pronounce all their words with their lips and tongue. Their letters are written sideways and number 24; when each of these are divided into two, they amount to 48; they have no other letters besides these, and they can write anything with these 48, which correspond to the Japanese *iroha* [1]. The Hollanders are very clever artisans and very skilful in designing various contrivances. They are the best seamen on the ocean seas in the whole world, well versed in astronomy, geography and divination. They are also first-class medical scientists. The Dutch ships which come to Nagasaki, do not come direct from Holland, but from Karabya [Java] and Siam etc. where they take in their cargoes for Nagasaki. Formerly these ships used to go to Hirado, but from Kwanei 18 (1641) they came to Nagasaki, since when they have come every year without interruption. They set sail from Java in the middle of the fifth month, and reach Nagasaki about the beginning of the 7th month. During the 8th and 9th month they drive trade, and their return is fixed by regulation for the 20th day of the 9th month. During this time the Captains change over, and the newly arrived one stays in Nagasaki, visiting the Yedo government in the spring of the following year. This happens annually. Their residence at Nagasaki is built on an isolated bit of land, and people are usually forbidden to enter it, but during the trade of the 8th and 9th months, merchants are permitted to go in and out.

Products.
Red woollen cloth. – cloth rashees (assorted sizes) – *raseita* – *saruze*[2] – kerseys *heruhetowan* – *kareita* – *saetsu* – armosyn – *herusai* – grofgreinen – satins (black & red) – *saai* – *buraata* – *regadouru* – *choroken* – *kabechoro* - *donsu* – *tabii* – satin – velvet – Dutch purses – Dutch brocade – brown striped cloth – gold embroidered calicoes – Dutch foil – gold leather – blue leather – russet leather – assorted leathers for purses, – crystal – coral – agate – amber – quicksilver – arsenic – azure blue pigments for paint –

---

[1] The Japanse *kana* equivalent of the ABC.
[2] I am uncertain of the exact translation of these words in italics.

indigo-stones to stop bleeding; when held in the hand the flow of blood is stopped – gall stones of oxen – gall stones of wild boars – *kirinketsu*-horn of unicorn; this horn is a very efficacious medicine– mummy; there are various explanations about this, and it is said that it is made from human flesh flavoured and kneaded[1] –*rusaran*, a wood grown in Sororu(?), and applied in case of various diseases. – *handecobra*, a kind of wood like a vine for warding off serpents (Portuguese *pão de cobra*?) – *surangasuten* (stone in serpent's head; applied to dissolve poisons) – *masonya* (a drug from Amboyna) – medicine for curing coughs (known as Dutch cough cure) – Dutch saffron, which resembles the bastard (false) saffron and is used as a substitute for ginseng – iron and steel – gold and silver – single beads and necklaces thereof – mats for incense burners (made from things like some sort of sea shells) – Glass (*biidoro*) [2]mirrors, big and small, the former measuring 2 by 3 *shaku* & the latter 4 or 5 *sun* by 1 *shaku* – glass ware (*biidoro dogu*), used for utensils and orna- ments – spectacles of several kinds, viz.: spectacles, telescopes, microscopes, magnifying glasses, coloured glasses & *ari megane*(?) – barometers (those of the type recently imported by the Hollan- ders are only toys and not the same as those of yore; it consists of a piece of wood about 1 *shaku* long with a glass tube attached to it; the water in the glass tube rises or falls according to the 4 seasons of Spring, Summer, Autumn and Winter; it is hung on a post and from it the seasons can be calculated; it is not an article of mer- chandize, and there are two kinds of them) – astronomical charts and globes (not in the trade) – world maps and globes (also not in the trade) – navigational charts (used by ships on the seas; not in the trade)[3] – vices [or cranes?] (This article consists of an iron pole in the centre of a stout piece of timber; when the wheel is turned the iron pole protrudes and lifts even houses; this is a very convenient article).

Metal lanterns (not in the trade) – armour and helmets (ditto) leather shields (ditto) – muskets (ditto) – swords (ditto) – knives (big and small, at all prices) – chronometers (an apparatus by which one can tell the hour of the day; those which strike the hours according to the Dutch method of counting time are called clocks) – compasses – earthenware (various kinds) – pencils (red & black) – imitation amber – artificial flowers – medical instruments – needles (for sewing) – paper (very thick quality) – *quatarente* (or

[1] mommie (monne; monie); a sweet scented balm from Arabia, used for medicinal purposes and embalming corpses.

[2] From the Portuguese *vidro*.

[3] The importation of this cartographical material is an interesting illustration of what has been stated on pp. 12–13 *n.* of the text.

quatorowan)¹; an instrument for observing the stars; not in the trade – astrolabium (reckoning seasons by means of sunrays; not in the trade) – *Giamante*² (also called *diaman*); mostly in purple and red colours; they do not break even if struck with a hammer; it is supposed to be a kind of quartz – pictures of various kinds – tortoiseshell – *Teriaka* (a drug universally applied in case of illness) – *Biriri* (made of fishes' blood and imported from Sarata) – domestic animals of various kinds – monkeys (large and small) –dogs (ditto)– *trombeta* (a thing like a *kappa* or water-sprite; its bones are used as medicine) – oily medicines (*azeitouna, haruname, terrementina,* clove-oil, *kohakuyu,* etc. used for medicines; further details unnecessary as they are known to every dealer) – liquors of various kinds (*chinta,* wines, mom beer, arrack, cinnamon wine, aquae-vita etc; they are all distilled and flavoured). – In addition to the foregoing, there are lots of drugs, plants, birds and beasts, small utensils, dry goods and so forth, but there is not space to describe them in detail. All of the above mentioned articles are not products of Holland, but are imported here by Dutch ships from their country of origin;³. The foreign ships visiting Nagasaki (with the exception of those of Chosen and Ryukyu) come in the 6th or 7th month during the South monsoon, and are therefore usually termed Summer and Autumn ships, whilst those vessels which arrive at other times are called Spring and Winter vessels. The Hollanders have commercial relations with thirty-five countries.

---

¹ Quadrant.

² Diamonds probably, though the Japanese sometimes applied the term to cut glass.

³ Lists of goods imported by the Hollanders into Japan during the XVIIth and XVIIIth centuries will be found on pp. 184–195 of my article in *Trans. As. Soc. Japan,* 1930; in Appendix IV of Dr. Feenstra Kuiper's *Japan en de Buitenwereld* and in the Batavian *Dagh-Registers, passim.*

APPENDIX II

HAYASHI SHIHEI'S EXPLANATORY INSCRIPTION TO HIS PRINT OF THE *Shellach* IN 1782

Holland, or as it is also called Horan, or Komo (*lit.* "Red-hair") is the name of one of the provinces of the Netherlands. Now the Netherlands lie in the extreme N.W. of Europe. This territory has seven Provinces and seventeen daimyo [1]. Holland is one of these seven Provinces. This may be compared, in our country, with Shikoku and Kyushu, etc. forming provinces out of the whole of Japan. Holland lies between 50° & 53° from the North Pole. It is a very cold country. These people have five outstanding features; the have high noses, blue eyes, red hair, white skins, and tall bodies. Their characters are called *retteru* (letter) and they are written horizontaly; they cannot be read by Japanese, Chinese or similar people. Their *buruku* (broeck = breeches) corresponds to and is worn like the Japanese *nomohiki*. Their coat is called *rokko* (rock) which answers to our *Jiban*. Their officials are called mandarins, and on ceremonial occasions wear a cloak corresponding to our *maru-kappa*. Their food is bread and wheaten flour, made like a *mochi* (rice-ball) and eaten roasted. Besides this, they are fond of fowls, meat and greasy foods. Furthermore they eat lots of raw *daikon* (radishes) [2].

This country lies a long way from Japan, – 13,000 *ri* by our reckoning. Of this distance from Japan to Java is 3,000 *ri*, whilst from Java to Holland is 10,000 *ri*. Now the Hollanders who come every year to Japan, all come from Java and none from Holland. Java has been conquered by the Hollanders who have their chief fortress at Batavia; this corresponds to the Red-hair settlement at Deshima in Japan. Java lies due South of Japan. Therefore they come in the rainy season of the fifth month with the South wind, and, after importing their products, leave again with the North wind in the ninth month. This is done regularly.

[1] This is an amusing identification of the Heeren Zeventien, or Seventeen Directors of the governing board of the V.O.C. from 1602–1798.

[2] A rather surprising statement, as foreigners have never been partial to this peculiar Japanese delicacy.

Now the Hollanders call their ships *skippu* (schip). Their build is very imposing. To begin with they make the ship's hull from big timbers; next they fix in crosswise, square blocks of chestnut-wood; then they caulk up the seams with pitch and tar. All the hull below the waterline is sheathed in lead. The ship's beam is 3 *jo*; length, 15 *jo*; draught, 3 *jo* 8 *shaku*. All are 3-decked ships, distance between decks, 9 *shaku*. Altogether there are 4 masts. The height of the main mast is 19 *jo*. There are 17 sails altogether, and 12 flags. The ship mounts more than 30 guns. Each gun fires a shot weighing 3 *kwan* [1].

Now the crew of these ships usually amount to 100 or more persons. Amongst them are the officers called captain, factor, skipper, koopman, pilot etc. who are all upper-class Hollanders. The people under them are called *matorosu* (matrozen) who are very low-class. Furthermore one lot of these lower-class people is called *swardo jongo* (swaerte jongen) being *kurombo* or blacks, and not natives of Holland. Coolies from Jacatara (Batavia), Boegis, Bouton, Timor, etc. are bought by the Hollanders and used as slaves. As they all come from tropical countries they are all very black. Again, every ship has her own name, such as *Zeedoin* (*Zeeduin*), *Sutabenissu* (*Stavenisse*), *Hoisutesupiki* (*Huis te Spijk*) and so forth. This corresponds to *So and so Maru* in Japanese [2].

Now the goods imported by these ships include sugar, sappan-wood, rattans, woollens, velvets, San Thomé (calicoes), *kaiki*, in-cense, drugs, cloves, jasmine, pepper, and also glass and spectacles. Besides these, curios, strange birds, and animals are also imported. Their provisions include oxen, pigs, poultry, geese and the like in enormous quantities. Furthermore, the goods they export from Japan include a million *kin* of copper (annually), regularly[3]. In addition, oil-paper umbrellas, pottery, lacquered wares, copper kettles, copper cash, dry goods, clothes, as well as *saké*, mustard, pickled *daikon* and fruits, etc., for provisions, all in large quantities. The ship with the cargo weighs about ten million *kin*.

Now that country has been in existence for 5,400 years. From the date of the first Hollander ruler till the present day, is 1776 years. There has been no change in the dynasty of the rulers. From Kwanei 17 (*ie*. 1640) when trade was first allowed, unbroken

---

[1] 1 *ri* = 3.937. metres; 1 *jo* = 3.030 metres; 1 *shaku* = 0.303 metres; 1 *kwan* = 3.75 kilogrammes.

[2] Of these vessels the *Zeeduin* came to Japan in 1776 and again i n the following year. The *Stavenisse* came in 1775 and 1776, whilst the *Huis te Spijk* made the same voyage in 1778 and 1779.

[3] 1 *kin* = 0.6 kilogrammes.

intercourse has continued for 143 years till this year. Written in the 2nd year of Tenmei (1782) [1].

Hayashi Shihei
of Sendai wrote
it for fun.
Toshima Denkichi
of Nagasaki
printed & published
it.

----

[1] This last paragraph is rather confused, apart altogether from the implied found-dation of the Oranje-Nassau dynasty in A.D. 6. The trade of the Hollanders in Japan was first settled at Hirado by permission of Ieyasu in 1609, but the reference in the text is to the establishment of the Dutch at Deshima in Kwanei 18 (not 17) or 1641.

APPENDIX III

AUTOGRAPH LETTER OF ISAAC TITSINGH TO NISHI KICHIROBEI,
CHINSURA, 18TH MARCH, 1787

Aan de Heer Kitsrofe,

Ik heb uwEd: brief gedateert 23 singuats van het vijfde jaar der nengo Tenmy [1] ontfange, en sie daar uyt met genoege dat myne vrienden my niet hebben vergeeten, gaarne had ik in 1785 aan alle geschreeven dog wierd daarin verhindert door veele beesigheden en de toebereidselen tot mijn aanstaande reis, ik heb dit in het jaar 1786 gedaan en twyffel niet of myne brieven die ik aan den Heer Famarq ter bestelling gaf zullen behoorlyk zyn besorgd, met vermaak herinner ik my de teid die ik op Decima doorbragt in het vertalen van veele weetenswaardige zaaken en de moeite door U genoomen om mij de huwelyks plegtigheeden uyt te leggen, [2] schoon ik verseekert ben dat uwe vorderingen in de hollandse taal na myn vertrek zyn toegenoomen twyffel ik niet of de brief aan my geschreeve door u self is opgesteld, ik versoek daarom myself te schryven zonder den brief door andere te laaten verbeeteren op dat ik daar uyt van jaar tot jaar sien mag, hoe seer gy in dezelve zyt toegenoomen.

Voor uwe geneegene wenschen omtrend my ben ik ten hoogste dankbaar, ik geniet hier alles wat een mensch in dit leeve kan verlangen, egter wenschte ik nog eens op Japan te zyn om myn weetlust te voldoen, en van veele zaaken, die my nog onbekend zyn, onderrigting te verlangen, het uytsigt daar toe is hopeloos, het enigst middel dat my overig blyft, is myne vrienden door brieven te raadpleegen, het geen ik jaarlyks zal onderhouden, in myn laaste brief heb ik om zo veele zaaken versoek gedaan dat ik geene nieuwe commissies durf opgeeven eer dat de vorige zyn beantwoord, het welk

[1] Tenmei 5 or 1785, Tenmei being the *Nengo* or Year-period from 1781–1788; *singuats* is probably meant for shingatsu, (*lit.* new month or January), or possibly *shigatsu*, fourth month.

[2] See the illustrations and descriptions of these in Titsingh's posthumous work, *Illustrations of Japan.*

ik met het eerste schip van Batavia te gemoed sie, mogelyk herin-
nert UW: zig, eenige reegels van een alfabeth voor my vertaalt te
hebben, dog dit ging tot de letter ta, waar van het laatste vaars is
Dakarete neroe zo ta no skede' [Dakarete neru zo tanoshii de.]
   Het byslaapen is aangenaam. [1]
ik wilde gaarne de uytlegging van de andere reegels ook hebben,
waartoe ik dat alfabeth heb uytgeschreeven, en hierneevens send,
gelief ider reegel eerst in het Japans te schryven gelyk hier boove
staad, en dan de vertaling daar onder, UEd siet hier door dat ik my
nog op het schryven van de Japanse taal toeleg, sussee soereba nani
gotomotassoe [2]. Hiernevens gaan voor UW.Ed: drie stukken ar-
mozynen welke ik versoek als den geringe blyk van aandenken te
willen aannemen, terwyl ik UW.Ed: van harte een bestendige
welstand veel genoege, en bevordering toewensch, ik beveel mij in
uwe vriendschap en verblyve met waare agting.

UWEdles Vriend en Welwenscher

Bengale
den 28 Maart   (get.) I. Titsingh
   1787

---

[1] This lewd jingle is possibly part of a popular if unorthodox method of learning
the *gojuon*, or fifty sounds of the native kana syllabary, arranged perhaps in the same
way as the classic *iroha*. It doubtless appealed to Titsingh as a confessed admirer of the
frail beauties inhabiting the Maruyama or licensed quarter of Nagasaki, as may be
gathered from the following extract from a French traveller who visited Titsingh at
Chinsura about this time . . . ." A en croire M. Titsingh, rien de si séduisant que les
créatures qui la meublent. Elles sont toujours jeunes et très-jolies, polies, spirituelles,
musiciennes, danseuses par excellence, en un mot des espèces de *Houris*, pleines de
grâces, d'agrémens et de talens. J'ai quelque soupçon" — adds the Frenchman somewhat shrewdly — "que cette description est un peu flattée par le bon gouverneur hol-
landois." (*Voyage au Bengale*, I, p. 256.).

[2] *Shussei sureba nanigoto mo tassuru*, " By diligent application one can achieve
anything". I am indebted to General J. C. Pabst and Mr. J. B. Snellen for assistance
in unravelling Titsingh's somewhat peculiar *romaji*.

APPENDIX IV

British Museum Add. Mss. 9393. Chronology of the Japanese & Chinese by Isaak Titsingh, formerly Chief for the Dutch Company in Japan & Embassador at the Court of Pekin. Member of the Royal Society London. printed at [blank] A° 1807.

TITSINGH'S DEDICATION OF HIS MSS. "CHRONOLOGY OF THE JAPANESE AND CHINESE" TO KUCHIKI MASATSUNA, DAIMYO OF FUKUCHIYAMA IN TAMBA PROVINCE

To
Koetsoeki Oki no Kami, Minamotto-no Masa Tsoena, Prince of Oki & Fikoetsi-Jama in Tamba-no Koeni.

Our last meeting in Jedo has been on the 9th of Sanguats, the 2nd year of Ten-my, — more than 25 years are accordingly elapsed: though our correspondence had been continued during my stay in India, my departure for Europe on the 8th year of Kwansy has put a stop to it. — the continual war has since been a much regretted but permanent obstacle — once only, the 16th of May 1801, I wrote to you from London, but not receiving an answer, I am in doubts about the safe delivery of my letter.

Your cordial support during my inquiries, had given you a right to expect that being back in Europe, some accounts wou'd already have been publish'd — dejection of spirits by the unhappy situation of my country, & by the direction there of India affairs on my arrival, and afterwards a wandering & dissipated life have prevented it, being settl'd at Paris to my wishes I began to mind it seriously — as a specimen I delight offering you in anticipation this Chronological detail — fulfilling my promise of dedicating it to you, I beg you will accept of it as a lasting proof of my gratitude, indeed who of your countrymen has a better claim to it? Your noble emulation to excell amongst them in all pursuits of Arts and Sciences — your fervent inquiries for all what concerns our hemisphere, & your progresses in the Dutch language, render you a competent judge on my work: as it is extremely difficult for any man who had never been to your Country, nor studied on the spot it's History & customs to express the true sense & energy of some occurencies in a translation, I have taken that task upon me, translating it into English & French, in order it might also properly appear among both those enlighten'd and powerful Nations. The translations of your National Annals, the Nipon-O-day-itze-ran, & of your composition the Sin-Sen-Sen-poe have reached you already the 3rd year of Ten-my — they will appear with a vast number of other topics in supplement of this volume, having collected during my stay in your happy country (the remembrance of which affords me a permanent delight) a sufficient stock of materials to pass the remainder of life usefully & with pleasure, putting them to order: Your belov'd aphorism of Kon-fee-tsoe, [Confucius]

> Itsoe wari wo
> fito ni wa in 'té
> tsoemi no besi
> kokoro no towaba
> ikaga kotai in [1]

an aphorism, so eagerly recommended to me, & so scrupulously observ'd through your book [2] will be my guide: conscious how much travellers, who have visited far distant countries are inclin'd to embellish their reports, you will remember my solemn promise not to mention in the least but what has been extracted from your most esteem'd works, or was grounded on undeniable authoritys, &c., on the accounts of people, deserving all credit, nothing in consequence of my own will be added to the principial — if ever I may be so fortunate to finish the whole, you will decide to what a degree the favourite maxim of Kon-foe-tsoe "genko mattakf Seizo"[3] has been observ'd.

Allow me however to propose to you some doubts, which arose during the arrangement of this Chronology, "is it not evident (I asked myself) the Japonese, so jealous about their neighbours the Chinese, have endeavour'd composing their own history to fill up many gappings, by prolonging the lives of their first Dayris?" What has induc'd me to this, was, the long life, and the excessive duration of the reign of many, from Zin-moe until Retszu- Ten-O, where a period of 1060 years is wholy occupied by but 17 Dayris.

[1] An easy thing it is to tell lies: but by what means is the conscience to be tranquiliz'd? (Titsingh's note).

[2] About the end of the year 1782 the Prince forwarded me a copy of this work, on the ancient copper coins of China, in 3 volumes, recently from the press — already was I far advanc'd in the translation, when he insisted to have it return'd, as he had discover'd some mistakes — the fear of being suspected by posterity of a willful imposition of untruth, prompted him to condemn the whole edition to the flames, — he order'd a new impression of it, of which he soon sent me a copy — a Dutch translation of it I had the pleasure to forward to him before my leaving Japan. (*Ibidem*).

Already he had favoured me with his description of the Japanese copper coins, written by his own hand. (*Ibidem*).

[3] Facts must agree with words. (*Ibidem*).

The live (*sic*) of Zin-moe [Jimmu] & the reigns of Koan, of Sei-nin [Suinin], & of Osin [Ojin], son of Tzuay-ten-O [Chuai Tenno] have struck me more particularly: the first died at the age of 127 years, the second reigned 102, the third 99 years, and the last, born according to your History, the last year of the reign of his father, or the year 200 of our Era, & dying the year 310, are too extraordinary events to deserve implicit credit: we will grant you, their chaste and frugal life had contributed much for protracting their days to a considerable length, but how comes it no one of their successors since Nintok-ten-O [Nintoku Tenno] has transgress'd the present usual period of human life? Permit me to recommend to your descernment the solution of this problem [1].

Accept my most ardent wishes for your constant happiness — may the highest station be already the reward of your distinguished merits, nothing will be more dear to me than the receipt of a letter from you, with some explanations on the vast number of questions occuring in my former ones — in this pleasant prospect I delight in professing to you, my permanent attachment & regard, signing myself as usually,

                                        Your Friend and Wellwisher,
Amsterdam the 7th of June 1807   I. Titsingh.

[1] Professor Murdoch aptly notes in this connection, — "It is refreshing to find that Titsingh was by no means inclined to take the early so-called Japanese History on trust, as Kaempfer had done, and as Siebold, Hoffman, and Rein subsequently did." (*History*, III, p. 547, *n*). Kuchiki had been dead five years when this dedication was written.

APPENDIX V

QUESTIONS	ANSWERS
1. What is the total of the English Expeditionary force destined for China?	In the spring of 1842, the English military and naval forces in China were

Off the Canton River
One ship of   72 guns
Two ships of 18 is 36 guns
One ship of   10 guns
two armed steamships

Off Amoy
One ship of 44 guns
One ,,   ,, 18 ,,
One ,,   ,, 10 ,,
One ,,   ,, 6 ,,

Off Chushan
One ship of 72 guns
One ,,   ,, 16 guns

Off Shanghai and Ningpo
One ship of   44 guns
Four ships each of 18 is   72 guns
One ship of   10 guns
four armed steamships

The total landing force, including infantry and artillery, comprises 4,000 men, European and Indian.

2. Do the English soldiers use a helmet and armour? Are cavalry units also included in the China Expeditionary force?

English curassiers (cavalry, horsemen) wear a helmet and cuirass, like the Dutch and French; but there are no cavalry amongst the English troops in China.

3. Are not the battles always fought on level ground? Is not the ground sometimes levelled artificially?

No, because you don't find level ground everywhere. China is a hilly land; and it is almost impossible to level its terrain.

4. Why have the Tartars lost, since they are said to be brave enough?

Bravery alone is not sufficient, the art of war demands something more. No outlandish power can compete with a European one, as can be seen by the great realm of China which has been conquered by only four thousand men.

5. Mortar or Howitzer, — which is used most? Do they both fire incendiary shot?

Both are used, — the mortar chiefly in siege-warfare, in order to start a fire. Incendiary shot is *not* used with a howitzer.

6. What artillery is damaging to English ships?

Shot of 24 lbs. calibre and above can be fired from a good distance and will pierce the hull of a ship and damage it seriously.

7. Do the English use steamboats principally?

Steamboats are used close inshore and for reconaissance in shallow water, for landing troops, and to cover their landing with gun fire. There are only six armed steamboats with the English forces in China, whereas there are sixteen other large and small warships, with a total of 410 cannon.

8. What is the shape of a steamboat?

In order to depict this clearly, I attach herewith a drawing of a medium sized steamship.

9. Can a steamboat continue on its course if it is fired on by artillery?

If it was hit in the engine, which is placed amidships, it could not continue under steam; but in that event the sails could be used, since a steamship is always provided with them.

10. Is the mast sometimes broken by a shot &c? Is the rigging burnt? What sort of protection is used on these occasions?

Oh yes! [*sic*]. It has happened more than once that a ship has been dismasted and unrigged.
In that event a jury rig and sails are hoisted, for which purpose an ample supply of cordage, sails and wood is always kept on board.

11. Is a strong wind, like we had on the 3rd of the ninth month, dangerous for a ship? Can a ship in such a strong wind navigate under full sail? Can the ship's boat go back and forth in such weather?

Stormy weather is always dangerous because it may work up to a typhoon, and this endangers a ship with its violent and irregular winds. Ships then bear only a little sail, or lie to, that is with the prow half into the wind, the foresail full, and the mizzen sail backed, — it then makes almost no progress but stays in that position until the wind abates.

12. Are such heavy winds ever met at sea?

In the offing of the Cape of Good Hope, one finds the heaviest storms in which the waves run as high as the heavens, — the storm which we had here on the 3rd of the ninth month was nothing in comparison.

13. Does a steamboat continue in such weather?

No, in such weather a steamboat lies to, and makes use of its sails.

14. Does New-Holland belong to England nowadays?

There are several English settlements on New-Holland, — but a large part of it is still unoccupied by any European nation [1].

---

[1] I owe a copy of this paper to Mr. Th. J. Odenkircher, of the Kantoor voor de Statistiek, Batavia, in 1933, one of whose ancestors was in Japan in 1842. For the impression made by the Opium War in Tokugawa Japan cf. the masterly essay of Dr. R. Van Gulik, *Kakkaron, a Japanese echo of the Opium War*, in *Monumenta Serica*, Vol. IV, pp. 478–545 (Peking, 1940).

APPENDIX VI

A

LIST OF THE TOKUGAWA SHOGUNS, 1603–1868

Name	Born	Nominated	Abdicated	Died
1. Ieyasu	1542	1603	1605	1616
2. Hidetada	1579	1605	1623	1632
3. Iemitsu.	1604	1623		1651
4. Ietsuna	1641	1651		1680
5. Tsunayoshi	1646	1680		1709
6. Ienobu	1662	1709		1712
7. Ietsugu.	1709	1712		1716
8. Yoshimune	1684	1716	1745	1751
9. Ieshige	1711	1745	1760	1761
10. Ieharu	1737	1760		1786
11. Ienari	1773	1786	1837	1841
12. Ieyoshi	1793	1837		1853
13. Iesada	1824	1853		1858
14. Iemochi	1846	1858		1866
15. Keiki	1837	1866	1868	190?

B

LIST OF THE NENGO OR YEAR-PRRIODS, 1696–1868

Keicho	1596–1615	Empo	1673–1681
Genwa	1615–1624	Tenwa	1681–1684
Kwanei	1624–1644	Teikyo	1684–1688
Shoho	1644–1648	Genroku	1688–1704
Keian.	1648–1652	Hoei	1704–1711
Shoo	1652–1655	Shotoku.	1711–1716
Meireki	1655–1658	Kyoho	1716–1736
Manji	1658–1661	Gembun	1736–1741
Kwambun	1661–1673	Kwampo	1741–1744

Eikyo	1744–1748	Kokwa	1844–1848
Kwanen	1748–1751	Kaei	1848–1854
Horeki	1751–1764	Ansei	1854–1860
Meiwa	1764–1772	Menen	1860–1861
Annei	1772–1781	Bunkyu	1861–1864
Tenmei	1781–1789	Gwanji	1864–1865
Kwansei	1789–1801	Keio	1865–1868
Kyowa	1801–1804	Meiji	1868–1912
Bunkwa	1804–1818	Taisho	1912–1926
Bunsei	1818–1830	Showa	1926–19
Tempo	1830–1844		

C

GLOSSARY OF JAPANESE WORDS

BAKUFU, "curtain government"; term commonly applied to the military or Shogunal government, so called because the commander's post in the field was usually screened off by screens or curtains. The term here is restricted to the Tokugawa regime of 1603–1868.

BUGYO, "bringer of gifts"; magistrate or governor appointed by the central government. Originally there were two of these officials for Nagasaki, of whom one resided at Yedo and the other at Nagasaki, relieving each other at intervals. In 1687 the number of Bugyo was raised to three, of whom two lived in Nagasaki, each taking his turn to be relieved by the third, who resided in Yedo. In 1700 four Bugyo were appointed, two of whom resided in Nagasaki and two in Yedo.

BUKE, military nobility or feudal lords.

BYOBU, pictorial screen, usually with a background of gold-leaf paper.

CHA-NO-YU, the tea cremony. CHAJIN is a devotee or connoisseur of the same. CHAIRO, tea-coloured, or very pale brown.

DAIKWAN, Shogunal Deputy or Commissioner. There was always one in Nagasaki.

DAIMYO, "great name"; head of a clan with a minimum revenue of 10,000 *koku* (bales) of rice.

DAIRI, originally a term used for that part of the palace specially reserved for the service of the Emperor. By extension, the word *dairi* was applied to the Emperor himself, and was commonly used in this way by Kaempfer, Titsingh and the old Hollanders. Compare "Sublime Porte" for the Sultan of Turkey.

E, generic term for any form of pictorial art, whether picture, drawing, painting, illustration, wood-cut, or colour-print. Here mainly used in the last sense. viz., — *Nagasaki-e* = Nagasaki colour-prints; *Yedo-e* = Yedo colour-prints (or *Ukiyoe*); *Kamigata-e* = prints made in Kyoto or Osaka; *Yoko-hama-e* = prints dealing with life in Yokohama, and so forth.

E-HON, a picture book.

EZU, drawing or illustration.

FUDE, Japanese writing or painting brush.

HAN, (1) A stamp or seal. (ii) A printing-block; wood-block. (iii) A print.

KAKEMONO, a hanging scroll, usually mounted on rollers.

KAMIGATA, Kyoto, Osaka and surrounding district.

KANGAKUSHA, classical Chinese scholar.

KARO, chief retainer or major-domo of a Daimyo's household.

KOMO, "Red-hair[s]". Popular nickname for the Hollanders.

MAKIMONO, pictorial scroll.

NAMBAN, "Southern Barbarian[s]"; term applied to the Portuguese.

RANGAKU, "Dutch Learning" or the study of Dutch.

RANGAKUSHA, Dutch Scholar; opposed to Kangakusha (a Classical Chinese scholar) or Wagakusha (native Japanese scholar) q.v.

ROJU, Great Council, or Cabinet; highest administrative council under the Shogunate.

RYU, School, style or method, in the artistic sense. e.g. Kano-ryu = the Kano School.

SAMURAI, feudal retainer; vassal of a daimyo.

SEIYO, Western World, Europe.

SHOGUN, Generalissimo or Commander-in-chief. Head of the military government of Japan before 1868.

TENNO, "Lord of Heaven". The Emperor.

UKIYOE, "Floating World"; school of popular art which originated at Yedo in the XVIIth century and attained its apogee at the end of the eighteenth and beginning of the nineteenth centuries.

WAGAKUSHA, native Japanese scholar.

YEDO-E, Yedo-style paintings or prints, see *Ukiyoe*.

YOKOHAMA-E, colour-prints depicting life in the foreign settlement at Yokohama *c.* 1860–1880, but made for the most part at Yedo (Tokyo).

ZU, generic term for drawing, picture, map or diagram. Usually used in the sense of map here.

———

ABRIDGED BIBLIOGRAPHY

A. *Books.*

ARAKI, K. *Bunkwa Inyu ni kansuru Kosho Tenrankai Mokuroku.* Osaka, 1925. (Quoted in the text of this essay as Araki's *Catalogue*).

CARON, *A true Description of the Mighty Kingdoms of Japan & Siam by François Caron and Joost Schouten. Reprinted from the English edition of 1663 with introduction, notes and appendixes by C. R. Boxer.* London, 1935. (Cf. also under Koda, S., *infra*).

DAGH-REGISTER *gehouden int Casteel Batavia vant passerende daer ter plaetse als over geheel Nederlandts India,* 1624–1683. 23 vols. Batavia and The Hague, 1887–1933.

DAM, P. VAN, *Beschrijvinge van de Oostindische Compagnie.* (ed. F. W. Stapel) 6 vols. The Hague, 1927–1943.

FEENSTRA-KUIPER, J. *Japan en de Buitenwereld in de achttiende eeuw.* The Hague, 1921.

IKENAGA, T. *Hosaibankwa Daihokan.* 2 vols. Osaka, 1933.

ITAZAWA, T. *Rangaku no igi to Rangaku ni kansuru ni san no mondai.* Series of articles in *Rekishi-Chiri* (q.v. under list of periodicals). Vol. 59, Tokyo, 1932.

—— *Oranda fusetsu-sho no kenkyu* (in *Nihon ko-bunka kenkyo-jo hokoku.* Vol. 3). Tokyo, 1937.

KAEMPFER, E. *The History of Japan.* 2 vols. London, 1728.

KIRKWOOD, K. *Renaissance in Japan, A cultural survey of the seventeenth century.* Tokyo, 1938.

KLEIWEG DE ZWAAN, J. P. *Völkerkundliches und Geschichtliches über die Heilkunde der Chinesen und Japaner mit besonderer Berücksichtigung Holländischer Einflüsse.* Haarlem, 1917.

KODA, S. *Oranda Yawa,* Tokyo, 1931.

—— *Oranda Zatsuwa,* Tokyo, 1934.

—— *Nihon Dai-O Kokushi. François Caron gencho.* Tokyo, 1948.

KOGA, J. *Nagasaki-shi.* Nagasaki, 1928.

KRIEGER, C. *The Infiltration of European civilization in Japan during the 18th century.* Leiden, 1940. (Cf. under Otsuki, *infra*).

KURODA, G. *Seiyo no eikyo wo uketaru Nihongwa.* Kyoto, 1924.
—— *Nagasaki-kei Yogwa.* Osaka, 1932.
MIKAMI, Y. and SMITH, D. E. *A History of Japanese Mathematics.* Chicago, 1914.
MODY, N. *A Collection of Nagasaki colour-prints and paintings showing the influence of Chinese and European Art on that of Japan.* 2 vols. Kobe and London, 1939.
MURAKAMI, N. *Deshima Rankan Nisshi.* 3 vols. Tokyo, 1938–1941.
—— *Nagasaki-shi shi. Tsuko-Boeki-hen. Seiyo sho-koku-bu.* Nagasaki, 1935.
MURAOKA, edition of the *Tenchi-Ridan* by Shiba Kokan. Tokyo, 1930.
MURDOCH, J. *A History of Japan.* Vol. III. *The Tokugawa Epoch,* 1652–1868. London, 1926.
NAGAMI, T. *Nagasaki no bijitsu-shi,* Tokyo, 1927.
—— *Nagasaki Hangwa-shu.* Tokyo, 1926.
—— *Zoku Nagasaki Hangwa-shu.* Tokyo, 1926.
NAGAYAMA, T. *Taigai shiryo bijitsu daikan.* Nagasaki, 1918.
OTANI, R. *Tadataka Ino, the Japanese Land-Surveyor.* Tokyo, 1932.
OTSUKI, J. *Shinsen Yogaku Nempyo.* Tokyo, 1927. (Translated by C. Krieger, q.v. *supra*).
PAPINOT, E. *Historical and Geographical Dictionary of Japan.* Tokyo, 1909; Ann Arbor, 1948.
SANSOM, G. *Japan. A Short Cultural History.* London, 1931 and 1946.
SHIMMURA, I. *Namban Koki.* Tokyo, 1925.
—— *Zoku Namban Koki.* Tokyo, 1925.
TITSINGH, I. *Illustrations of Japan.* London, 1822.
VALENTYN, F. *Oud en Nieuw Oost-Indien.* 8 vols. Dordrecht and Amsterdam, 1724–26.
WIJNAENDTS VAN RESANDT, W. *De Gezaghebbers der Oost-Indische Compagnie op hare buiten-comptoiren in Azië* (Amsterdam, 1944).

B. *Periodicals*

Mittheilungen der Deutschen Gesellschaft für Natur-und Völkerkunde Ostasiens. Yokohama and Tokyo. Series from 1873 to 1941, including 2 vols. of the *Jubilaümsband,* published in 1933.
Monumenta Nipponica. Studies on Japanese Culture, Past and Present. 6 vols. Tokyo, 1938–1943.
Rekishi-Chiri. (*History-Geography*). Tokyo, 1899–1941.

Shigaku-Zasshi (Zeitschrift für Geschichtswissenschaft). Tokyo, 1872–1941.

T'oung Pao. Archives concernant l'histoire, les langues, la géographie l'éthnographie et les arts de l'Asie Orientale. Leiden, 1890–1949.

Transactions of the Asiatic Society of Japan. Yokohama and Tokyo, 1872–1940.

Transactions and Proceedings of the Japan Society. London, 1892–1941.

Verhandelingen van het Bataviaasch Genootschap van Kunsten en Wetenschappen. Batavia, 1779–1941.

ADDENDA TO BIBLIOGRAPHY OF THE 1950 EDITION

Since the publication of the 1950 edition of this book, the following works have appeared which are relevant to one or another of the topics discussed in the text.

BEANS, G. H., *A List of Japanese maps of the Tokugawa era* (Jenkintown, Pa., 1951).

BOWERS, J. Z., *Medical Education in Japan. From Chinese Medicine to Western Medicine* (New York and London, 1965).

GLAMANN, K., *Dutch-Asiatic Trade, 1620–1740* (The Hague, 1958).

HALL, J.W., *Tanuma Okitsugu, 1719–1788* (Harvard University Press, 1955).

KEENE, D., *The Japanese discovery of Europe. Honda Toshiaki and other discoverers, 1720–1798* (London, 1952).

ROESSINGH, M. P. H., *The Archive of the Dutch Factory in Japan, 1609–1860* (The Hague, 1964).

SANSOM, G., *The Western World and Japan: a study in the interaction of European and Asiatic cultures* (New York & London, 1950).

VEENHOVEN, W. A., *Strijd om Deshima. Een onderzoek naar de aanslagen van Amerikaanse, Engelse en Russische zijde, op het Nederlandse Handelsmonopolie in Japan, 1800–1817* (Bloemendaal, 1950).

VOLKER, T., *Porcelain and the Dutch East India Company, as recorded in the Dagh-Registers of Batavia, Hirado, and Deshima, 1602–1682* (Leiden, 1954).

VOLKER, T., *The Japanese porcelain trade of the Dutch East India Company after 1683* (Leiden, 1959).

INDEX

INDEX

Udagawa, Gensui, (1755–1797), 49
Umemura, Yaeyemon, 118

Valentyn, François, Extracts from translated into Japanese, 122–3, 131
Valverde, 48
Verstegen, Willem, 4 n
Vesalius, 48
Villeneuve, de, 93, 133
Vries, Maerten Gerritszoon, 5–6, 40 n

Waeijen, Jacob van der, 50
Wakasugi, Isohachi, 101–103
Watanabe, Shuseki, 124
Wataya, 94
Whitney, Dr., 44 n, 47 n
Wieder, F., Dr. 2 n
Woolf (Hans Wolfgang Braun von Ulm), Swabian gunner, 32–5

Yakken, 66
Yakken Hanrei, 66
Yamada Emonsaku, 95–6
Yamatoya, 74–5, 92–3, 107, 108
Yedo Halma, 65–6
Yochi Ryaku Zetsu, 21
Yoi Shinsho, 49
Yokohama-e, 70
Yonjuni Koku Jinbutsu Zusetzu, 17–18
Yoshida, Jikyu, 44
Yoshikawa, 65
Yoshimune, eighth Tokugawa Shogun, 12, 13, 41–3, 50; and alleged ban on Dutch books, 53–4, 61–2, 127, 139
Yoshio, Kosaku, 45, 126

Zoho Kwai Tsusho-ko, 11, 17
Zoho Rangaku Hai, 65